A-Level Year 1 & AS

Physics

Exam Board: OCR A

Revising for Physics exams is stressful, that's for sure — even just getting your notes sorted out can leave you needing a lie down. But help is at hand...

This brilliant CGP book explains **everything you'll need to learn** (and nothing you won't), all in a straightforward style that's easy to get your head around. We've also included **exam questions** to test how ready you are for the real thing.

There's even a free Online Edition you can read on your computer or tablet!

How to get your free Online Edition

Go to **cgpbooks.co.uk/extras** and enter this code...

```
3345 5602 6861 3453
```

This code only works for one person. If somebody else has used this book before you, they might have already claimed the Online Edition.

A-Level r̶e̶v̶i̶s̶i̶o̶n̶?̶ ̶I̶t̶ ̶h̶a̶s̶ ̶t̶o̶ be CGP!

Contents

Published by CGP

Editors:
David Maliphant, Rachael Marshall, Sam Pilgrim, Frances Rooney, Charlotte Whiteley and Sarah Williams

Contributors:
Tony Alldridge, Jane Cartwright, Peter Cecil, Mark Edwards, Barbara Mascetti, John Myers, Andy Williams

ISBN: 978 1 78294 295 5

With thanks to Mark Edwards, Ian Francis and Glenn Rogers for the proofreading.
With thanks to Jan Greenway for the copyright research.

Data used to construct stopping distance diagram on page 27 From the Highway Code.
© Crown Copyright re-produced under the terms of the Open Government licence
http://www.nationalarchives.gov.uk/doc/open-government-licence/version/3/

Clipart from Corel®
Printed by Elanders Ltd, Newcastle upon Tyne.

Based on the classic CGP style created by Richard Parsons.

The Scientific Process

'How Science Works' is all about the scientific process — how we develop and test scientific ideas. It's what scientists do all day, every day (well, except at coffee time — never come between a scientist and their coffee).

Scientists Come Up with **Theories** — Then **Test Them**...

Science tries to explain **how** and **why** things happen — it **answers questions**. It's all about seeking and gaining **knowledge** about the world around us. Scientists do this by **asking** questions, **suggesting** answers and then **testing** their suggestions to see if they're correct — this is the **scientific process**.

1) **Ask** a question about **why** something happens or **how** something works.
   E.g. what is the nature of light?

2) **Suggest** an answer, or part of an answer, by forming a **theory**
   (a possible **explanation** of the observations) — e.g. light is a wave.
   (Scientists also sometimes form a **model** too — a **simplified picture** of what's physically going on.)

3) Make a **prediction** or **hypothesis** — a **specific testable statement**, based on the theory, about what will happen in a test situation. For example, if light is a wave, it will interfere and diffract when it travels through a small enough gap.

4) Carry out a **test** — to provide **evidence** that will support the prediction (or help to disprove it). E.g. Young's double-slit experiment (p.86-87).

The evidence supported Quentin's Theory of Flammable Burps.

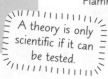

A theory is only scientific if it can be tested.

...Then They **Tell** Everyone About Their **Results**...

The results are **published** — scientists need to let others know about their work. Scientists publish their results in **scientific journals**. These are just like normal magazines, only they contain **scientific reports** (called papers) instead of the latest celebrity gossip.

1) Scientific reports are similar to the **lab write-ups** you do in school. And just as a lab write-up is **reviewed** (marked) by your teacher, reports in scientific journals undergo **peer review** before they're published.

2) The report is sent out to **peers** — other scientists that are experts in the **same area**. They examine the data and results, and if they think that the conclusion is reasonable it's **published**. This makes sure that work published in scientific journals is of a **good standard**.

3) But peer review **can't guarantee** the science is **correct** — other scientists still need to **reproduce** it.

4) Sometimes **mistakes** are made and bad work is published. Peer review **isn't perfect** but it's probably the best way for scientists to self-regulate their work and to publish **quality reports**.

...Then **Other Scientists** Will **Test** the Theory Too

Other scientists read the published theories and results, and try to **test the theory** themselves. This involves:

- Repeating the **exact same experiments**.
- Using the theory to make **new predictions** and then testing them with **new experiments**.

If the **Evidence** Supports a Theory, It's **Accepted** — for Now

1) If all the experiments in all the world provide good evidence to back it up, the theory is thought of as **scientific 'fact'** (for now).

2) But it will never become **totally indisputable** fact. Scientific **breakthroughs or advances** could provide new ways to question and test the theory, which could lead to **new evidence** that **conflicts** with the current evidence. Then the testing starts all over again...

And this, my friend, is the **tentative nature of scientific knowledge** — it's always **changing** and **evolving**.

The Scientific Process

So scientists need evidence to back up their theories. They get it by carrying out experiments, and when that's not possible they carry out studies. But why bother with science at all? We want to know as much as possible so we can use it to try and improve our lives (and because we're nosy).

Evidence Comes From Controlled Lab Experiments...

1) Results from **controlled experiments** in **laboratories** are great.

2) A lab is the easiest place to **control variables** so that they're all **kept constant** (except for the one you're investigating).

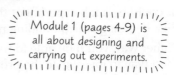

Module 1 (pages 4-9) is all about designing and carrying out experiments.

...That You can Draw Meaningful Conclusions From

1) You always need to make your experiments as **controlled** as possible so you can be confident that any effects you see are linked to the variable you're changing.

2) If you do find a relationship, you need to be careful what you conclude. You need to decide whether the effect you're seeing is **caused** by changing a variable (this is known as a **causal relationship**), or whether the two are just **correlated**. There's more about drawing conclusions on page 9.

"Right Geoff, you can start the experiment now... I've stopped time..."

Society Makes Decisions Based on Scientific Evidence

1) Lots of scientific work eventually leads to **important discoveries** or breakthroughs that could **benefit humankind**.

2) These results are **used by society** (that's you, me and everyone else) to **make decisions** — about the way we live, what we eat, what we drive, etc.

3) All sections of society use scientific evidence to make decisions, e.g. politicians use it to devise policies and individuals use science to make decisions about their own lives.

Other factors can **influence** decisions about science or the way science is used:

Economic factors

Society has to consider the **cost** of implementing changes based on scientific conclusions — e.g. the cost of reducing the UK's carbon emissions to limit the human contribution to **global warming**.

Scientific research is often **expensive**. E.g. in areas such as astronomy, the Government has to **justify** spending money on a new telescope rather than pumping money into, say, the **NHS** or **schools**.

Social factors

Decisions affect **people's lives** — e.g. when looking for a site to build a **nuclear power station**, you need to consider how it would affect the lives of the people in the **surrounding area**.

Environmental factors

Many scientists suggest that building **wind farms** would be a **cheap** and **environmentally friendly** way to generate electricity in the future. But some people think that because **wind turbines** can **harm wildlife** such as birds and bats, other methods of generating electricity should be used.

So there you have it — how science works...

Hopefully these pages have given you a nice intro to how science works, e.g. what scientists do to provide you with 'facts'. You need to understand this, as you're expected to know how science works yourself — for the exam and for life.

Planning and Implementing

Science is all about getting good evidence to support (or disprove) your theories, so scientists need to be able to spot a badly designed experiment, interpret the results of an experiment or study, and design their own experiments too...

You Might have to **Design an Experiment** to Answer a **Question**

1) You might be asked to design a physics experiment to **investigate** something or answer a question.

2) It could be a **lab experiment** that you've seen before, or something **applied**, like deciding which building material is best for a particular job.

3) Either way, you'll be able to use the physics you know and the skills in this topic to figure out the best way to investigate the problem.

A **Variable** is Anything that has the Potential to **Change** in an Experiment

1) First, you need to identify your **independent** and **dependent variables**:

> The **independent** variable is the thing you **change**.
> The **dependent** variable is the thing you **measure**.

Example 1: If you're investigating how changing the potential difference across a component affects the current through it, the **independent variable** is the **potential difference**, and the **dependent variable** is the **current**.

2) Apart from the independent and dependent variables, **all other variables** should stay the same during your experiment. If not, you can't tell whether or not the independent variable is responsible for any changes in your dependent variable, so your results won't be **valid** (p.8). This is known as **controlling variables**. It might be worth **measuring control variables** that are likely to change during your experiment to check that they really are under control.

Example 1 (continued): In the example above, you need to use the same **circuit components**, and to keep the **temperature** of the apparatus **constant** — e.g. by letting the circuit cool down between readings.

Example 2: If you're investigating the value of **acceleration due to gravity** by dropping an object and timing its fall, **draughts** in the room could really mess up your results. Picking an object that is more **resistant** to being blown about (like a ball-bearing) will help make your results more **precise** and therefore more **valid** (p.8).

Select Appropriate **Apparatus** and **Techniques**

1) You need to think about what **units** your measurements of the independent and dependent variables are likely to be in before you begin (e.g. millimetres or metres, milliseconds or hours).

2) Think about the **range** you plan on taking measurements over too — e.g. if you're measuring the effect of increasing the force on a spring, you need to know whether you should increase the force in steps of 1 newton, 10 newtons or 100 newtons. Sometimes, you'll be able to **estimate** what effect changing your independent variable will have, or sometimes a **pilot experiment** might help.

3) Considering your measurements before you start will also help you choose the most appropriate **apparatus** and **techniques** for the experiment:

> There's a whole range of apparatus and techniques that could come up in your exam. Make sure you know how to use all the ones you've come across in class.

Example:

- If you're measuring the length of a **spring** that you're applying a force to, you might need a **ruler**. If you're measuring the diameter of a **wire**, you'd be better off with a set of **callipers**.

  If the extension will be small, the wire you use might be **too long** to suspend vertically from a clamp. You might need to use a pulley like in the Young modulus experiment on p.48.

- If you're measuring a **time interval**, you could use a **stopwatch**. If the time is **really short** (for example if you're investigating acceleration due to gravity), you might need something more sensitive, like **light gates**.

4) Whatever apparatus and techniques you use, make sure you use them **correctly**. E.g. if you're measuring a length, make sure your eye is level with the ruler when you take the measurement.

5) While you're planning, you should also think about the **risks** involved in your experiment and how to manage them — e.g. if you're investigating a material that might snap, wear safety goggles to protect your eyes.

Planning and Implementing

Figure Out how to *Record* your Data Before you *Start*

Before you get going, you'll need a **data table** to record your results in.

1) It should include space for your **independent variable** and your **dependent variable**. You should specify the **units** in the headers, not within the table itself.

2) Your table will need enough room for repeated measurements. You should aim to **repeat** each measurement at least **three times**. Taking repeat measurements can reduce the effect of random errors in your results (see p.12) and makes spotting **anomalous** results, like this one, much easier.

3) There should be space in your table for any data processing you need to do, e.g. calculating an **average** from repeated measurements, or calculating speed from measurements of distance and time.

4) Most of the time, your data will be **quantitative** (i.e. you'll be recording numerical values). Occasionally, you may have to deal with **qualitative** data (data that can be observed but not measured with a numerical value). It's still best to record this kind of data in a table, to keep your results **organised**, but the layout may be a little **different**.

| | Current / A | | | |
P.d. / V	Trial 1	Trial 2	Trial 3	Average
1.00	0.052	0.047	0.050	0.050
1.50	0.079	0.075	0.077	0.077
2.00	0.303	0.098	0.097	...
2.50	0.129	0.125	0.130	...
3.00	0.149	0.151	0.145	...
...	...	...	...	...

You Could be Asked to *Evaluate* An *Experimental Design*

If you need to evaluate an experimental design, whether it's your own or someone else's, you need to think about these sorts of things:

- Does the experiment **actually test** what it sets out to test?
- Is the method **clear** enough for someone else to follow?
- Apart from the **independent** and **dependent variables**, is everything else going to be **properly controlled**?
- Are the **apparatus** and **techniques appropriate** for what's being measured? Will they be used correctly?
- Are enough **repeated measurements** going to be taken?
- Is the experiment going to be conducted **safely**?

Greta was paying the price for not planning her experiment properly.

Practice Questions

Q1 What is meant by the term independent variable? What is a dependent variable?

Q2 Why do you need to plan to control all of the other variables in an experiment?

Q3 What do you need to consider when selecting your apparatus?

Q4 Why should you take repeated measurements in an experiment?

Exam Question

Q1 A student is investigating the effect of the light level on the resistance of an LDR (light-dependent resistor). The student connects the LDR to a power supply, and measures the resistance of the LDR at various distances from a light source using a multimeter.

a) State the independent and dependent variables for this experiment. [1 mark]

b) State two variables that the student needs to control in order to ensure his results are valid. [2 marks]

The best-planned experiments of mice and men...

...often get top marks. The details of planning and carrying out an experiment will vary a lot depending on what you're investigating, but if all this stuff is wedged in your brain you shouldn't go far wrong, so make sure you've got it learned.

Analysing Results

You've planned an experiment, and you've got some results (or you've been given some in your exam).
Now it's time to look into them a bit more closely...

Do any **Calculations** You Need to **First**

1) Before you calculate anything, check for any **anomalous results.** If there's something in the results that's **clearly wrong**, then don't include it in your calculations — it'll just **muck everything up.** Be careful though, you should only exclude an anomalous result if you have **good reason** to think it's wrong, e.g. it looks like a decimal point is in the **wrong place**, or you suspect that one of the control variables **changed**. And you should talk about any anomalous results when you're evaluating the experiment (pages 8-9).

2) For most experiments, you'll at least need to calculate the mean (average) of some **repeated measurements**:

$$\text{mean (average) of a measurement} = \frac{\text{sum of your repeated measurements}}{\text{number of repeats taken}}$$

In class, you could use a spreadsheet to process your data (and plot graphs), but it's important that you know how to do it by hand for the exam.

3) Calculate any quantities that you're interested in that you haven't **directly measured** (e.g. pressure, speed).

You should try to give any values you calculate to the **same number of significant figures** as the data value with the **fewest significant figures** in your calculation, **or one more** where it's sensible. If you give your result to too many significant figures, you're saying your final result is more **precise** than it actually is (see p.8).

Present Your Results on a **Graph**

Make sure you know how to plot a graph of your results:

If you need to use your graph to measure something, select axes that will let you do this easily (e.g. by measuring the gradient or the intercept, see the next page).

1) Usually, the **independent variable** goes on the **x-axis** and the **dependent variable** goes on the **y-axis**. Both axes should be **labelled** clearly, with the quantity and **units**. The **scales** used should be sensible (i.e. they should go up in sensible steps, and should spread the data out over the full graph rather than bunching it up in a corner).

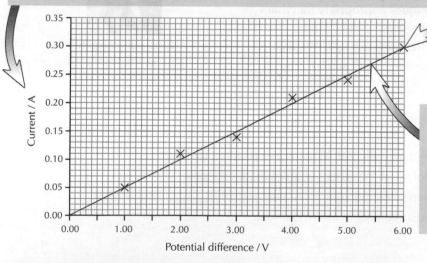

2) Plot your points using a **sharp pencil**, to make sure they're as **accurate** as possible.

3) Draw a **line of best fit** for your results. Around **half** the data points should be above the line, and half should be below it (you should ignore anomalous results). Depending on the data, the line might be **straight**, or **curved**.

Graphs can Show Different Kinds of **Correlation**

Remember, correlation does not necessarily mean cause — p.3.

The **correlation** describes the relationship between the variables. Data can show:

Positive correlation:
As one variable increases the other increases.

Negative correlation:
As one variable increases the other decreases.

No correlation:
No relationship between the variables.

Analysing Results

You Might Need to Find a Gradient or Intercept

If the line of best fit is **straight**, then the graph is **linear**. This means a change in one always leads to a change in the other.
The **line of best fit** for a linear graph has the **equation**: $y = mx + c$ Where *m* is the **gradient** of the line and *c* is the *y*-intercept.

If the line of best fit goes through the origin (c is 0), you can say the variables are **directly proportional** to each other: $y \propto x$ $\propto$ just means 'is directly proportional to'.

Example: This graph shows displacement against time for a motorbike travelling west. Find the bike's velocity.

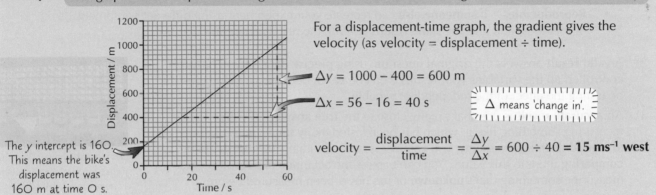

For a displacement-time graph, the gradient gives the velocity (as velocity = displacement ÷ time).

$\Delta y = 1000 - 400 = 600$ m

$\Delta x = 56 - 16 = 40$ s Δ means 'change in'.

The *y* intercept is 160. This means the bike's displacement was 160 m at time 0 s.

$$\text{velocity} = \frac{\text{displacement}}{\text{time}} = \frac{\Delta y}{\Delta x} = 600 \div 40 = \textbf{15 ms}^{-1} \textbf{ west}$$

If a graph has a **curved** line of best fit, you can find the gradient of a given point on the line by drawing a **tangent** to the curve (see page 23). It's sometimes helpful to choose axes that turn a curved graph into a straight one:

Example:

For a given force, the graph of **pressure** applied against the **area** that the force is applied over looks like this:

If you plot pressure against 1 ÷ area, the graph looks like this: 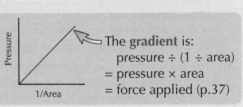 The **gradient** is:
pressure ÷ (1 ÷ area)
= pressure × area
= force applied (p.37)

Practice Questions

Q1 Describe what you should do with anomalous results when processing data.

Q2 How do you calculate an average of repeated results?

Q3 Sketch a graph showing a negative correlation.

Exam Question

Q1 An engineer is investigating the performance of a prototype car with a new kind of environmentally-friendly engine.
The data below shows the speed of the car, going from stationary to over 70 kilometres per hour.
(In this question, you may use the formula: acceleration = change in speed ÷ time taken to change speed.)

Time / s	0	2	4	6	8	10	12	14	16
Speed / km per hour	0	3	8	24	36	52	66	69	71

a) Draw a graph showing speed against time for this data. [4 marks]

b) State the times between which the graph is linear. [1 mark]

c) Using the graph, calculate the maximum acceleration of the car. [4 marks]

My level of boredom is proportional to the time I've spent on this page...

This stuff can get a bit fiddly, especially measuring the gradient of a curved line, but for the most part it's not too bad, and you should have seen a lot of it before. So dust off your pencil sharpener, and get to work...

Evaluating and Concluding

Once you've drawn your graphs and analysed your results, you need to think about your conclusions.

Evaluate the Quality of Your Results

Before you draw any conclusions, you should think about the quality of the results — if the quality's not great you won't be able to have much confidence in your conclusion. Good results are **precise**, **valid** and **accurate**.

1) The smaller the **range** that your data is spread over, the more **precise** it is.
A **precise** result is one that is **repeatable** and **reproducible**.

Precision is sometimes called reliability.

- **Repeatable** — **you** can **repeat** an experiment multiple times and get the **same results**. For experiments, doing more repeats enables you to assess how precise your data are — the **more repeats** you do, and the more **similar** the results of each repeat are, the more **precise** your data.

- **Reproducible** — if **someone else** can recreate your experiment using different equipment or methods, and gets the **same results** you do, the results are reproducible.

2) A **valid result** answers the **original question**, using **precise data**. If you haven't controlled all the variables your results won't be valid, because you won't just be testing the effect of the independent variable.

3) An **accurate result** is one that's really close to the **true answer**. If you're measuring something like g, which has been tested many times, and is known to a good degree of certainty, you can assess how accurate your results are by **comparing** them to this value. You can't assess the accuracy of a result if your measuring something that's **unknown** or has never been measured before.

David might have taken the suggestion that he repeat his experiment a bit far...

All Results have Some Uncertainty

1) **Every** measurement you take has an **experimental uncertainty**. The smallest uncertainty you can have in a measurement is ± **half** of one division on the measuring instrument used. E.g. using a thermometer with a scale where each division represents 2 °C, a measurement of 30 °C will at **best** be measured to be **30 ± 1 °C**. And that's without taking into account any other errors that might be in your measurement.

2) The ± sign gives you the **range** in which the **true** length (the one you'd really like to know) probably lies. 30 ± 0.5 cm tells you the true length is very likely to lie in the range of 29.5 to 30.5 cm. The maximum difference between your value and the true value (here 0.5 cm) is sometimes called the **margin of error**.

3) The smaller the uncertainty in a result or measurement, the smaller the range of possible values the result could have and the more precise your data can be. There are two measures of uncertainty you need to know about:

Absolute uncertainty — the **total uncertainty** for a measurement.
Percentage error — the uncertainty given as a **percentage** of the measurement.

Example: The resistance of a filament lamp is given as 5.0 ± 0.4 Ω. Give the absolute uncertainty and the percentage error for this measurement.

There's more about different types of errors and how to do calculations with uncertainty on page 12.

The **absolute uncertainty** is **0.4 Ω**.
To get the percentage error, just convert this to a percentage of the lamp's resistance: (0.4 ÷ 5) × 100 = **8%**

4) The uncertainty on a **mean** (see p.6) of repeated results is equal to **half the range** of the results.
E.g. say the repeated measurement of a current gives the results 0.5 A, 0.3 A, 0.3 A, 0.3 A and 0.4 A. The range of these results is 0.5 – 0.3 = 0.2 A, so the uncertainty on the mean current would be **± 0.1 A**.

Significant Figures give Uncertainties

If no uncertainty is given for a value, the **assumed uncertainty** is **half the increment** of the **last** significant figure that the value is **given** to. E.g. 2.0 is given to 2 **significant figures**, so you would assume an uncertainty of 0.05.

You should always assume the **largest** amount of uncertainty when doing an experiment, so make sure you keep an eye on the **significant figures** when taking measurements, doing calculations and evaluating uncertainties.

Evaluating and Concluding

Draw **Conclusions** that Your Results **Support**

1) A conclusion **explains** what the data shows. You can only draw a conclusion if your data **supports** it.

2) Your conclusion should be limited to the **circumstances you've tested** it under — if you've been investigating how the current flowing through a resistor changes with the potential difference across it, and have only used potential differences between 0 and 6 V, you can't claim to know what would happen if you used a potential difference of 100 V, or if you used a different resistor.

3) You also need to think about how much you can **believe** your conclusion, by evaluating the quality of your results (see previous page). If you can't believe your results, you can't form a **strong conclusion**.

Think About how the Experiment Could be **Improved**

Having collected the data, is there anything you think should have been done **differently**?
Were there any **limitations** to your method?

1) If the results aren't **valid**, could you change the experiment to fix this, e.g. by changing the data you're collecting?

2) If the results aren't **accurate**, what could have caused this?
Systematic errors (p.12) can affect accuracy — are there any that you could prevent?

3) Are there any changes you could make to the **apparatus** or **procedure** that would make the results more **precise**?

- The **less random error** there is in the measurement, the more **precise** your results.
  Increasing the number of **repeats** could help to reduce the **effect** of random errors in your results.

- By using the most **appropriate** equipment — e.g. swapping a millimetre ruler for a micrometer to measure the diameter of a wire — you can instantly cut down the **random error** (p.12) in your experiment.

- You can also use a **computer** to collect data — e.g. using light gates to measure a time interval rather than a **stopwatch.** This makes results more **precise** by reducing **human error**.

4) Are there any other ways you could have **reduced the errors** in the measurements?

Practice Questions

Q1 What is a valid result?

Q2 What is the difference between saying the results of an experiment are precise and saying that they are accurate?

Q3 What should you think about when you are trying to improve an experimental design?

Exam Questions

Q1 The resistance of a fixed resistor is given as 50.00 Ω.
According to the manufacturer, there is a 0.02% uncertainty in this value.
What is the minimum possible resistance of the resistor in Ω, to 2 decimal places?

   A: 49.00 Ω   B: 49.99 Ω   C: 49.90 Ω   D: 49.09 Ω   [1 mark]

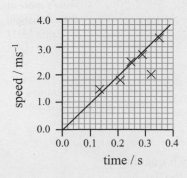

Q2 A student is investigating how the speed of a falling object is affected by how long it has been falling for. He drops an object from heights between 10 cm and 60 cm and measures its speed at the end of its fall, and the time the fall takes, using light gates. He plots a graph of the final speed of the object against the time it took to fall, as shown on the left.

a) Identify the anomalous result.   [1 mark]

b) The student concludes that the speed of any falling object is always proportional to the time it has been falling for.
Explain whether or not the results support this conclusion.   [2 marks]

In conclusion, Physics causes headaches...

Valid, precise, and accurate... you'd think they all mean the same thing, but they really don't.
Make sure you know the difference, and are careful about which one you use, or you'll be throwing marks away.

Quantities and Units

Learning Physics is a lot like building a house — both involve drinking a lot of tea. Also, both have important foundations — if you skip this stuff everything else is likely to go a bit wrong. So, here goes brick-laying 101...

A **Physical Quantity** has both a **Numerical Value** and a **Unit**

1) Every time you measure something or calculate a quantity you need to give the **units**.

2) The **Système International** (S.I.) includes a set of **base units** for physical quantities from which lots of other units are derived. Here are the S.I. base units that you need to know:

Quantity	S.I. base unit
mass	kilogram, kg
length	metre, m
time	second, s
current	ampere, A
temperature	kelvin, K
amount of a substance	mole, mol

Kilograms are a bit odd — they're the only S.I. unit with a scaling prefix (see the next page).

You're more likely to see temperatures given in °C.

3) Many more units can be derived from these base units — e.g. newtons, N, for force are defined by $kg\,ms^{-2}$. The newton is an **S.I. derived unit**.

4) The S.I. derived units you'll need will be covered throughout the book and you need to remember them.

5) You also need to have a rough idea of the size of each S.I. base unit and S.I. derived unit in this book, so that you can **estimate quantities** using them.

Remembering how S.I. derived units are defined will help you make sure the other quantities in your equations are in the right units.

You Can **Check** Your Units **Mathematically**

The units in any equation must always be the **same on both sides** — this is called **homogeneity of units**. You can use this rule to work out some of the simpler S.I. derived units, like speed:

Example: Show that the S.I. derived unit for speed is ms^{-1}.

You know that speed = distance ÷ time

Distance is a length, so its S.I. base unit is the metre, m.

The base unit of time is the second, s.

To find the unit for speed, just put the units for distance and time into the equation for speed: **m ÷ s = ms^{-1}**

They always checked the homogeneity of their outfits before leaving the house.

You can also use this rule to help you to **check your working** if you have to combine or rearrange equations:

Example: For an object moving with uniform acceleration, $v = u + at$ and $s = \frac{1}{2}(u + v)t$. Combine these equations to get an equation for s in terms of u, v and a. Check the homogeneity of your answer.

There's more about these equations on pages 16-17.

Rearrange $v = u + at$ to get: $t = \frac{v - u}{a}$

The substitute this into $s = \frac{1}{2}(u + v)t$ $\Rightarrow$ $s = \frac{1}{2}(u + v)\left(\frac{v - u}{a}\right)$

v = final velocity, u = initial velocity, a = acceleration, t = time and s = displacement

Then simplify the equation: $s = \frac{1}{2a}(v^2 - u^2)$

To check the units are the same on both sides, substitute the units for each quantity into the equation, then cancel down (you can ignore any numbers, e.g. the 2):

s is a length in metres, v and u are velocities in ms^{-1} and a is acceleration in ms^{-2}.

$m = \frac{1}{ms^{-2}}((ms^{-1})^2 - (ms^{-1})^2) = \frac{1}{ms^{-2}}(m^2s^{-2} - m^2s^{-2})$

There are only metres left on both sides of the equation, so the equation is homogeneous.

Quantities and Units

Prefixes Let You Scale Units

Physical quantities come in a **huge range** of sizes. Prefixes are scaling factors that let you write numbers across this range without having to put everything in standard form.

These are the prefixes you need to know:

prefix	pico (p)	nano (n)	micro (μ)	milli (m)	centi (c)	deci (d)	kilo (k)	mega (M)	giga (G)	tera (T)
multiple of unit	1×10^{-12}	1×10^{-9}	1×10^{-6}	0.001 (1×10^{-3})	0.01 (1×10^{-2})	0.1 (1×10^{-1})	1000 (1×10^{3})	1×10^{6}	1×10^{9}	1×10^{12}

If you're a bit uncertain about moving between these scaling factors, then convert quantities into the standard unit before you do anything else with them:

Example 1: Convert 1869 picometres into nanometres.

First, convert the value to metres: $1869 \text{ pm} = 1869 \times 10^{-12} \text{ m}$

Then divide by 1×10^{-9} to convert to nanometres: $1869 \times 10^{-12} \div 1 \times 10^{-9} = \textbf{1.869 nm}$

Or, you can convert between prefixes directly:

Example 2: Convert 0.247 megawatts into kilowatts.

$1 \text{ MW} = 1 \times 10^{6} \text{ W}$ and $1 \text{ kW} = 1 \times 10^{3} \text{ W}$

So the scaling factor to move between MW and kW is:

$(1 \times 10^{6}) \div (1 \times 10^{3}) = 1 \times 10^{3}$

So $0.247 \text{ MW} = 0.247 \times 1 \times 10^{3} = \textbf{247 kW}$

> It's really easy to get muddled up when you're converting between prefixes. The rule is, if you're moving to the right in the table above, your number should get smaller, and if you're moving to the left the number should get larger. If your answer doesn't match the rule, you've made a mistake.

Be careful with using these prefixes in the middle of calculations — they'll change the units of your final answer, and could get you in a mess. It's generally safest to do your calculations with everything in its S.I. or S.I. derived units, then convert the answer to include a sensible prefix when you're done.

Practice Questions

Q1 What is the S.I. unit of mass?
Q2 What is meant by an S.I. base unit and an S.I. derived unit?
Q3 What does the term homogeneity of units mean?
Q4 What is: a) 20 000 W in kilowatts, b) 2×10^{-6} W in milliwatts c) 1.23×10^{7} W in gigawatts?

Exam Question

Q1 The density, ρ, of a material gives its mass per unit volume. It is given by $\rho = m/V$, where m = mass and V = volume.

a) Express the units of density in terms of S.I. base units. [1 mark]

b) Calculate the density of a cube of mass 9.8 g, and side length 11 mm. Give your answer in the units stated in part a). [2 marks]

What's the S.I. base unit for boring...

Not the most exciting pair of pages these, I'll admit, but it's important that you have the basics down, or else you're leaving yourself open to simple little mistakes that'll cost you marks. So make sure you've memorised all the S.I. units in the table, then try and write down all the prefixes and their scaling factors. If you don't get them all first time, keep trying until you can. Remember, you need to know the units for every other quantity you meet in this book, too.

Measurements and Uncertainties

There are errors and uncertainties in every measurement. You need to know how to deal with them...

Uncertainty is Caused by Random and Systematic Errors

Every measurement you take has an experimental uncertainty (p.8) caused by two types of error:

1) **Systematic errors** (including **zero errors**) are the same every time you repeat the experiment (they shift all the values by the same amount). They may be caused by the **equipment** you're using or how it's **set-up**, e.g. not lining up a ruler correctly when measuring the extension of a spring. Systematic errors are really **hard to spot**, and they affect the **accuracy** of your results. It's always worth **checking your apparatus** at the start of an experiment, e.g. measure a few known masses to check that a mass meter is **calibrated** properly.

2) **Random errors** vary — they're what make the results a bit different each time you repeat an experiment. If you measured the length of a wire 20 times, the chances are you'd get a slightly different value each time, e.g. due to your head being in a slightly different position when reading the scale. It could be that you just can't keep controlled variables (p.4) exactly the same throughout the experiment. Using **more sensitive apparatus** can reduce random errors, so your results can be more **precise** (p.8) and **repeating measurements** can reduce the effect of random errors.

Sometimes You Need to Combine Uncertainties

You have to combine the uncertainties of different measured values to find the uncertainty of a calculated result:

Adding or Subtracting Data — ADD the Absolute Uncertainties

Example: A wire is stretched from 0.3 ± 0.1 cm to 0.5 ± 0.1 cm. Calculate the extension of the wire.

1) First subtract the lengths without the uncertainty values: $0.5 - 0.3 = 0.2$ cm
2) Then find the total uncertainty by adding the individual absolute uncertainties: $0.1 + 0.1 = 0.2$ cm
So, the extension of the wire is **0.2 ± 0.2 cm**.

Multiplying or Dividing Data — ADD the Percentage Uncertainties

Example: A force of 15 N $\pm 3\%$ is applied to a stationary object which has a mass of 6.0 ± 0.3 kg. Calculate the acceleration of the object and state the percentage uncertainty in this value.

1) First calculate the acceleration without uncertainty: $a = F \div m = 15 \div 6.0 = 2.5$ ms^{-2}
2) Next, calculate the percentage uncertainty in the mass: % uncertainty in $m = \dfrac{0.3}{6.0} \times 100 = 5\%$
3) Add the percentage uncertainties in the force and mass values to find the total uncertainty in the acceleration: Total uncertainty $= 3\% + 5\% = 8\%$
So, the acceleration $= $ **2.5 ms^{-2} $\pm 8\%$**

Raising to a Power — MULTIPLY the Percentage Uncertainty by the Power

Example: The radius of a circle is $r = 40$ cm $\pm 2.5\%$. What will the percentage uncertainty be in the area of this circle (πr^2)?

The radius will be raised to the power of **2** to calculate the area.
So, the percentage uncertainty will be $2.5\% \times 2 = $ **5%**

Percentage uncertainty (or percentage error) is on page 8.

Percentage Difference Shows How Close Your Answer is to the True Value

If you know the **true value** of what you're investigating you can measure the **accuracy** of your result using **percentage difference**. This is the difference between your value and the true value, **expressed as a percentage** of the true value. Don't get it confused with percentage uncertainty (p.8).

Measurements and Uncertainties

Error Bars *Show the* **Uncertainty** *of* **Individual Points**

1) Most of the time, you work out the **uncertainty** in your **final** result using the uncertainty in **each measurement** you make.

2) When you're plotting a **graph**, you can show the uncertainty in **each measurement** by using **error bars** to show the **range** the point is likely to lie in. E.g. the error bars on the graph on the right show the error in each measurement of the extension of an object when a force is applied.

3) You can have error bars for both the dependent and the independent variable.

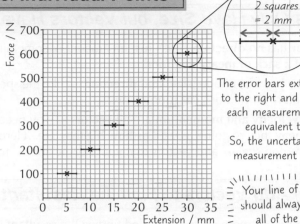

2 squares = 2 mm

The error bars extend 2 squares to the right and to the left for each measurement, which is equivalent to 2 mm. So, the uncertainty in each measurement is ± 2 mm.

Your line of best fit (p.6) should always go through all of the error bars.

You Can **Calculate** the **Uncertainty** of **Final Results** from a **Line of Best Fit**

Normally when you draw a graph you'll want to find the **gradient** or **intercept** (p.7). For example, you can calculate k, the **force constant** of the object being stretched, from the **gradient** of the graph on the right — here it's about 20 000 Nm^{-1}. You can find the **uncertainty** in that value by using **worst lines**:

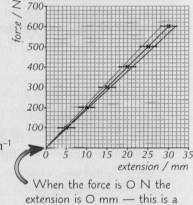

1) Draw lines of best fit which have the **maximum** and **minimum** possible slopes for the data and which should go through all of the **error bars** (see the pink and blue lines on the right). These are the **worst lines** for your data.

2) Calculate the **worst gradient** — the gradient of the slope that is **furthest** from the gradient of the line of best fit. The blue line's gradient is about 21 000 Nm^{-1} and the pink line's gradient is about 19 000 Nm^{-1}, so you can use either here.

3) The **uncertainty** in the gradient is given by the **difference** between the **best** gradient (of the line of best fit) and the **worst gradient** — here it's 1000 Nm^{-1}. So this is the uncertainty in the value of the force constant. For this object, the force constant is 20 000 ± 1000 Nm^{-1} (or 20 000 Nm^{-1} ± 5%).

When the force is O N the extension is O mm — this is a measurement with no uncertainty.

4) Similarly, the uncertainty in the **y-intercept** is just the **difference** between the **best** and **worst** intercepts (although there's no uncertainty here since the best and worst lines both go through the origin).

Practice Questions

Q1 Give two examples of possible sources of random error and one example of a possible source of systematic error in an experiment. Which kind of error is least likely to affect the precision of the results?

Q2 What is meant by percentage difference?

Q3 What are worst lines? How could you use them to find the uncertainty in the intercept of a graph?

Exam Question

Q1 A student is investigating the acceleration of a remote controlled car. The car has an initial velocity of 0.52 ± 0.02 ms^{-1} and accelerates to 0.94 ± 0.02 ms^{-1} over an interval of 2.5 ± 0.5 s.

a) Calculate the percentage uncertainty in the car's initial speed. [1 mark]

b) Calculate the percentage uncertainty in the car's final speed. [1 mark]

c) Calculate the car's average acceleration over this interval. Include the absolute uncertainty of the result in your answer. (acceleration = change in velocity ÷ time taken). [4 marks]

My percentage uncertainty about these pages is 99.99%...

Uncertainties are a bit of a pain, but they're really important. Learn the rules for combining uncertainties, and make sure you don't get percentage uncertainty and percentage difference confused. Random and systematic errors are an exam favourite too, so make sure you know the difference, and how to minimise both in your experiments.

Scalars and Vectors

And now time to draw some lovely triangles. Please, don't all thank me at once...

Scalars Only Have Size, but Vectors Have Size and Direction

1) A **scalar** has **no direction** — it's **just an amount** of something, like the **mass** of a **sack of meaty dog food**.

2) A **vector** has magnitude (**size**) and **direction** — like the **speed and direction** of next door's **cat** running away.

3) **Force**, **velocity** and **momentum** are all **vectors** — you need to know **which way** they're going as well as **how big** they are. Here are some of the common scalars and vectors that you'll come across in your exams:

Scalars	Vectors
mass, time, temperature, length, speed, energy	displacement, force, velocity, acceleration, momentum

You can Add Vectors to Find the Resultant

1) Adding two or more vectors is called finding the **resultant** of them. Whatever the quantity is — displacement, force, momentum, the procedure is the same.

2) You should always start by drawing a **diagram**. Draw the vectors '**tip to tail**'. If you're doing a **vector subtraction**, draw the vector you're subtracting with the same magnitude but pointing in the **opposite direction**.

3) If the vectors are at **right angles** to each other, then you can use **Pythagoras** and **trigonometry** to find the resultant vector.

4) If the vectors aren't at right angles, you may need to draw a **scale diagram**.

Trig's really useful in physics, so make sure you're completely okay with it. Remember SOH CAH TOA.

Example 1: Jemima goes for a walk. She walks 3.0 m north and 4.0 m east. She has walked 7.0 m but she isn't 7.0 m from her starting point. Find the magnitude and direction of her displacement.

First, draw the vectors **tip-to-tail**. Then draw a line from the **tail** of the first vector to the **tip** of the last vector to give the **resultant**:

Because the vectors are at right angles, you get the **magnitude** of the resultant using Pythagoras:

$R^2 = 3.0^2 + 4.0^2 = 25.0$ So $R = \textbf{5.0 m}$

Now find the **bearing** of Jemima's new position from her original position. You use the triangle again, but this time you need to use trigonometry. You know the opposite and the adjacent sides, so you can use:

$\tan \theta = 4.0 / 3.0$ So $\theta = \textbf{053°}$ **(to 2 s.f.)**

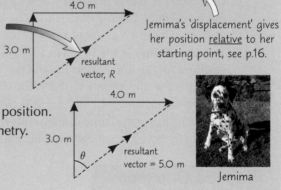

Jemima's 'displacement' gives her position relative to her starting point, see p.16.

Jemima

Example 2: A van is accelerating north, with a resultant force of 510 N. A wind begins to blow on a bearing of 150°. It exerts a force of 200 N on the van. What is the new resultant force acting on the van?

A bearing is just an angle measured clockwise from the north line, represented by three digits, e.g. 10° = 010°.

The vectors **aren't** at right angles, so you need to do a scale drawing. Pick a sensible scale. Here, 1 cm = 100 N seems good.

Using a really sharp pencil, draw the initial resultant force on the van. As the van is going north, this should be a 5.1 cm long line going straight up.

The force of the wind acts on a bearing of 150°, so add this to your diagram. Using the same scale, this vector has a length of 2.0 cm.

Then you can draw on the new resultant force and measure its length. Measure the angle carefully to get the bearing.

The resultant force has a magnitude of 350 N (to 2 s.f.), acting on a bearing of 017° (to 2 s.f.).

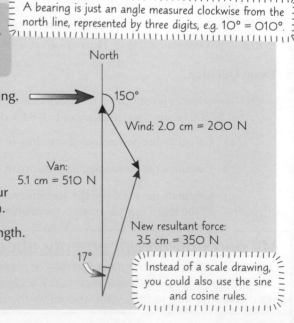

Instead of a scale drawing, you could also use the sine and cosine rules.

Scalars and Vectors

It's Useful to Split a *Vector* into *Horizontal* and *Vertical Components*

This is the opposite of finding the resultant — you start from the resultant vector and split it into two **components** at right angles to each other. You're basically **working backwards** from Example 1 on the last page.

Resolving a vector *v* into horizontal and vertical components:

You get the **horizontal** component v_h like this:

$$\cos \theta = v_h / v$$

$$\boxed{v_h = v \cos \theta}$$

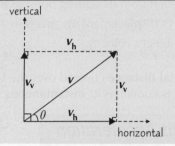

...and the **vertical** component v_v like this:

$$\sin \theta = v_v / v$$

$$\boxed{v_v = v \sin \theta}$$

Where θ is the angle from the horizontal.

Example: Charley's amazing floating home is travelling at a speed of 5 ms^{-1} at an angle of 60° up from the horizontal. Find the vertical and horizontal components.

The **horizontal** component v_h is:

$v_h = v \cos \theta = 5 \cos 60° = $ **2.5 ms^{-1}**

The **vertical** component v_v is:

$v_v = v \sin \theta = 5 \sin 60° = $ **4.3 ms^{-1} (to 2 s.f.)**

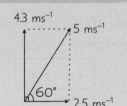

Charley's mobile home was the envy of all his friends.

Resolving is dead useful because the two components of a vector **don't affect each other**. This means you can deal with the two directions **completely separately**.

It also gives you another way to find the resultant vector of two vectors that aren't at **right angles** to each other. **Resolve the vectors** into their horizontal and vertical components, and add up the vertical and horizontal components separately. Then you just need to **combine** the two to get the resultant vector. It can be a lot less fiddly than drawing accurate scale diagrams.

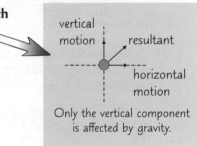

Only the vertical component is affected by gravity.

Practice Questions

Q1 What is the difference between a vector and a scalar? Give three vector quantities and three scalar quantities.

Q2 Describe how to find a resultant vector using a scale diagram.

Exam Questions

Q1 The wind applies a horizontal force of 20 N on a falling rock of weight 75 N.
Calculate the magnitude and direction of the resultant force. [2 marks]

Q2 A glider is travelling at a velocity of 20.0 ms^{-1} at an angle of 15.0° below the horizontal.
Calculate the horizontal and vertical components of the glider's velocity. [2 marks]

Q3 A remote controlled boat is placed in a river. The boat produces a driving speed of 1.54 ms^{-1} at an angle of 60° to the current (travelling with the current). The river is flowing at 0.20 ms^{-1}.
By resolving the vectors into their horizontal and vertical components, show that the resultant velocity of the boat is 1.6 ms^{-1} at an angle of 54° to the current. [4 marks]

I think I'm a scalar quantity, my Mum says I'm completely direction-less...

Lots of different ways to solve vector problems on these pages, it must be your lucky day. Personally, I avoid doing scale drawings unless I absolutely have to (too fiddly for my liking), but if they work for you that's great. And you may get told to draw one in your exams, so you need to be prepared in case they come up.

Motion with Constant Acceleration

All the equations on this page are for motion with constant acceleration. It makes life a whole lot easier, trust me.

Learn the **Definitions** of **Speed**, **Displacement**, **Velocity** and **Acceleration**

Displacement, velocity and acceleration are all **vector** quantities (page 14), so the **direction** matters.

> **Speed** — How fast something is moving, regardless of direction.
> **Displacement** (s) — How far an object's travelled from its starting point in a given direction.
> **Velocity** (v) — The rate of change of an object's displacement (its speed in a given direction).
> **Acceleration** (a) — The rate of change of an object's velocity.

During a journey, the **average speed** is just the **total distance** covered over the **total time** elapsed.
The speed of an object at any given point in time is known as its **instantaneous** speed.

Uniform Acceleration is Constant Acceleration

Acceleration could mean a change in speed or direction or both.

Uniform means **constant** here. It's nothing to do with what you wear.
There are **four main equations** that you use to solve problems involving **uniform acceleration**. You need to be able to **use them**, but you don't have to know how they're **derived** — we've just put it in to help you learn them.

1) **Acceleration is the rate of change of velocity.**
From this definition you get:

$$a = \frac{(v - u)}{t} \quad \text{so} \quad \boxed{v = u + at}$$

where:
u = initial velocity a = acceleration
v = final velocity t = time taken

2) **s = average velocity × time**
If acceleration is constant, the average velocity is just the average of the initial and final velocities, so:

$$\boxed{s = \frac{(u + v)}{2} \times t} \quad s = \text{displacement}$$

3) Substitute the expression for v from equation 1 into equation 2 to give:

$$s = \frac{(u + u + at) \times t}{2}$$
$$= \frac{2ut + at^2}{2}$$

$$\boxed{s = ut + \tfrac{1}{2}at^2}$$

4) You can **derive** the fourth equation from equations **1** and **2**:

Use equation **1** in the form: $a = \dfrac{v - u}{t}$ Multiply both sides by s, where: $s = \dfrac{(u + v)}{2} \times t$

This gives us: $as = \dfrac{(v - u)}{t} \times \dfrac{(u + v)t}{2}$

The t's on the right cancel, so:
$$2as = (v - u)(v + u)$$
$$2as = v^2 - uv + uv - u^2$$

so: $\boxed{v^2 = u^2 + 2as}$

Example: A tile falls from a roof 25 m high. Calculate its speed when it hits the ground and how long it takes to fall. Take $g = 9.81\ \mathrm{ms^{-2}}$.

First of all, write out what you know:
$s = 25$ m
$u = 0\ \mathrm{ms^{-1}}$ since the tile's stationary to start with
$a = 9.81\ \mathrm{ms^{-2}}$ due to gravity
$v = ?$ $t = ?$

Usually you take upwards as the positive direction. In this question it's probably easier to take downwards as positive, so you get $g = +9.81\ \mathrm{ms^{-2}}$ instead of $g = -9.81\ \mathrm{ms^{-2}}$.

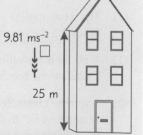
9.81 ms⁻²   25 m

Then, choose an equation with only **one unknown quantity**.
So start with $v^2 = u^2 + 2as$
$v^2 = 0 + 2 \times 9.81 \times 25$
$v^2 = 490.5$ $v = \mathbf{22.1\ ms^{-1}}$ (to 3 s.f.)

Now, find t using:
$s = ut + \tfrac{1}{2}at^2$
$25 = 0 + \tfrac{1}{2} \times 9.81 \times t^2$
$t^2 = \dfrac{25}{4.905}$

Final answers:
$t = \mathbf{2.26\ s}$ (to 3 s.f.)
$v = \mathbf{22.1\ ms^{-1}}$ (to 3 s.f.)

Motion with Constant Acceleration

Example: A car accelerates steadily from rest at a rate of 4.2 ms⁻² for 6 seconds.
   a) Calculate the final speed.
   b) Calculate the distance travelled in 6 seconds.

Remember — always start by writing down what you know.

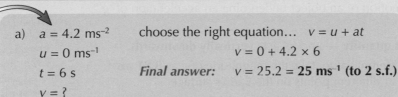

a) $a = 4.2$ ms⁻²   choose the right equation... $v = u + at$
   $u = 0$ ms⁻¹ $v = 0 + 4.2 \times 6$
   $t = 6$ s   *Final answer:* $v = 25.2 = \mathbf{25}$ **ms⁻¹ (to 2 s.f.)**
   $v = ?$

b) $s = ?$ you can use: $s = \dfrac{(u + v)t}{2}$ or: $s = ut + \frac{1}{2}at^2$
   $t = 6$ s
   $u = 0$ ms⁻¹
   $a = 4.2$ ms⁻² $s = \dfrac{(0 + 25.2) \times 6}{2}$ $s = 0 + \frac{1}{2} \times 4.2 \times (6)^2$
   $v = 25.2$ ms⁻¹

                    Final answer: $s = \mathbf{76}$ **m (to 2 s.f.)** $s = \mathbf{76}$ **m (to 2 s.f.)**

You Have to **Learn** the Constant Acceleration **Equations**

Make sure you learn the equations. There are only four of them and these questions are always dead easy marks in the exam, so you'd be dafter than a hedgehog in a helicopter not to learn them...

Practice Questions

Q1 Write down definitions for speed, displacement, average velocity, instantaneous velocity and acceleration.
Q2 Write out the four constant acceleration equations.

Exam Questions

Q1 A skydiver jumps from an aeroplane when it is flying horizontally. She accelerates due to gravity for 5 s.
   a) Calculate her maximum vertical velocity. (Assume no air resistance.)   [2 marks]
   b) Calculate how far she falls in this time.   [2 marks]

Q2 A motorcyclist slows down uniformly as he approaches a red light.
   He takes 3.2 seconds to come to a halt and travels 40 m in this time.
   a) Calculate how fast he was travelling initially.   [2 marks]
   b) Calculate his acceleration. (N.B. a negative value shows a deceleration.)   [2 marks]

Q3 A stream provides a constant acceleration of 6 ms⁻². A toy boat is pushed directly against the current
   and then released from a point 1.2 m upstream from a small waterfall. Just before it reaches the waterfall,
   it is travelling at a speed of 5 ms⁻¹.
   a) Calculate the initial velocity of the boat.   [2 marks]
   b) Calculate the maximum distance upstream from the waterfall the boat reaches.   [2 marks]

Q4 A cyclist is travelling at a constant speed of 3 ms⁻¹ as he starts to roll down a hill. He rolls down the
   hill with a constant acceleration. During the third second, he travels a distance of 6 m.
   a) Calculate the cyclist's acceleration.   [2 marks]
   b) Calculate how far he travels during the 4th second.   [1 mark]

Constant acceleration — it'll end in tears...

If a question talks about "uniform" or "constant" acceleration, it's a dead giveaway they want you to use one of these equations. The tricky bit is working out which one to use — start every question by writing out what you know and what you need to know. That makes it much easier to see which equation you need. To be sure. Arrr.

Free Fall

So, how do you work this parachute thing agaiAAAAAaaaaaarrrrrrggggghhhhhhhhhhhhhhh...

Free Fall is when there's Only Gravity and Nothing Else

Free fall is defined as "the motion of an object undergoing an acceleration of '*g*'".
You need to remember:

1) Acceleration is a **vector quantity** — and '*g*' acts **vertically downwards**.
2) Unless you're given a different value, take the magnitude of *g* as **9.81 ms⁻²**, though it varies slightly at different points on the Earth's surface.
3) The **only force** acting on an object in free fall is its **weight**.
4) Objects can have an initial velocity in any direction and still undergo **free fall** as long as the **force** providing the initial velocity is **no longer acting**.

> *g* is also used for gravitational field strength, where $g = 9.81$ Nkg⁻¹ (p.32). If you break down Nkg⁻¹ into S.I. units, they are actually the same as ms⁻², so it's the same '*g*'.

You Can Measure g by using an Object in Free Fall

You don't have to do it this way — but if you don't know a method of measuring *g* already, learn this one.

You need to be able to:

1) **Sketch** a diagram of the **apparatus**.
2) **Describe** the **method**.
3) **List** the **measurements** you make.
4) **Explain** how '*g*' is **calculated**.
5) Be aware of sources of **error**.

Another gravity experiment.

Experiment to Measure the Acceleration Due to Gravity

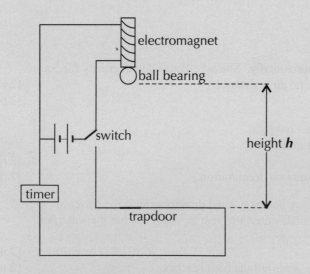

electromagnet

ball bearing

switch

height *h*

timer

trapdoor

> In this experiment you have to assume that the effect of air resistance on the ball bearing is negligible and that the magnetism of the electromagnet decays instantly.

The Method:

1) Measure the height *h* from the **bottom** of the ball bearing to the **trapdoor**.
2) Flick the switch to **simultaneously** start the timer and disconnect the electromagnet, releasing the ball bearing.
3) The ball bearing falls, knocking the trapdoor down and breaking the circuit — which stops the timer.

Use the time *t* measured by the timer, and the height *h* that the ball bearing has fallen, to calculate a value for *g*, using $h = \frac{1}{2}gt^2$ (see next page for more on acceleration formulas).

> By using a computer, errors in the timing are reduced — human error can be introduced when using a stopwatch.

The most **significant** source of error in this experiment will be in the measurement of *h*. Using a ruler, you'll have an uncertainty of about 1 mm.

This dwarfs any error from switch delay or air resistance.

> You could reduce the error in your measurement of *h* by using a set square to make sure your eye is level with the ruler.

Free Fall

You can Just Replace a with g in the Equations of Motion

You need to be able to work out **speeds**, **distances** and **times** for objects in **free fall**. Since g is a **constant acceleration** you can use the **constant acceleration equations**. But g acts downwards, so you need to be careful about directions.

To make it clear, there's a sign convention: **upwards is positive, downwards is negative**.

> **Sign Conventions — Learn Them:**
> g is always <u>downwards</u> so it's <u>usually negative</u> t is <u>always positive</u>
> u and v can be either <u>positive or negative</u> s can be either <u>positive or negative</u>

Case 1: No initial velocity (it just falls)

Initial velocity $u = 0$

Acceleration $a = g = -9.81$ ms^{-2}

So the constant acceleration equations become: $\implies$

$$v = gt \qquad v^2 = 2gs$$
$$s = \tfrac{1}{2}gt^2 \qquad s = \tfrac{vt}{2}$$

Case 2: An initial velocity upwards (it's thrown up into the air)

The constant acceleration equations are just as normal,
but with $a = g = -9.81$ ms^{-2}

Case 3: An initial velocity downwards (it's thrown down)

Example: Alex throws a stone down a cliff. She gives it a downwards velocity of 2 ms^{-1}.
It takes 3 s to reach the water below. How high is the cliff?

1) You know $u = -2$ ms^{-1}, $a = g = -9.81$ ms^{-2} and $t = 3$ s. You need to find s.

s will be negative because the stone ends up further down than it started.

2) Use $s = ut + \tfrac{1}{2}gt^2 = (-2 \times 3) + (\tfrac{1}{2} \times -9.81 \times 3^2) = -50.145$ m.

The cliff is 50 m high (to 2 s.f.)

Practice Questions

Q1 What is the value of the acceleration of a free-falling object?

Q2 What is the initial velocity of an object which is dropped?

Q3 Describe how you would find a value for g by using a trapdoor and electromagnet set-up.

Exam Questions

Q1 A student has designed a device to estimate the value of 'g'. It consists of two narrow strips
of card joined by a piece of transparent plastic. The student measures the widths of the strips
of card then drops the device through a light gate connected to a computer.
As the device falls, the strips of card break the light beam.

a) Give three pieces of data that the student will
need from the computer to estimate g. [3 marks]

b) Explain how these measurements can be used to estimate 'g'. [3 marks]

c) Give one reason why the student's value of 'g' will not be entirely accurate. [1 mark]

Q2 Charlene is bouncing on a trampoline. She reaches her highest point a height of 5 m above the trampoline.
Assume air resistance is negligible.

a) Calculate the speed with which she leaves the trampoline surface. [2 marks]

b) Calculate how long it takes Charlene to reach her highest point. [2 marks]

c) Calculate her velocity as she lands back on the trampoline. [1 mark]

It's not the falling that hurts — *it's the* being pelted with rotten vegetables... okay, okay...

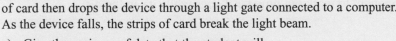

The hardest bit with free fall questions is getting your signs right. Draw yourself a little diagram before you start doing any calculations, and label it with what you know and what you want to know. That can help you get the signs straight in your head. It also helps the person marking your paper if it's clear what your sign convention is. Always good.

Projectile Motion

Any object given an initial velocity and then left to move freely under gravity is a projectile, which handily you can predict the motion of by resolving its velocity. If you're doing Maths, you might have to cover this again there. Double the fun.

You have to think of **Horizontal** and **Vertical** Motion **Separately**

In projectiles, the **horizontal** and **vertical** components of the object's motion are **completely independent**. Projectiles follow a **curved path** because the horizontal velocity remains **constant**, while the vertical velocity is affected by the **acceleration due to gravity**, g.

Example: Sharon fires a scale model of a TV talent show presenter horizontally with a velocity of 100 ms^{-1} from 1.5 m above the ground. How long does it take to hit the ground, and how far does it travel horizontally? Assume the model acts as a particle, the ground is horizontal and there is no air resistance.

Think about vertical motion first:

1) It's **constant acceleration** under gravity...

2) You know $u = 0$ (no vertical velocity at first), $s = -1.5$ m and $a = g = -9.81$ ms^{-2}. You need to find t.

3) Use $s = \frac{1}{2}gt^2 \Rightarrow t = \sqrt{\frac{2s}{g}} = \sqrt{\frac{2 \times -1.5}{-9.81}} = 0.553...$ s

4) So the model hits the ground after **0.55 (to 2 s.f.)** seconds.

(diagram: $a = 0$, $u = 0$, $a = g$ with curved path)

Then do the horizontal motion:

1) The horizontal motion isn't affected by gravity or any other force, so it moves at a **constant speed**.

2) That means you can just use good old **speed = distance / time**.

3) Now $v_h = 100$ ms^{-1}, $t = 0.553...$ s and $a = 0$. You need to find s_h.

4) $s_h = v_h t = 100 \times 0.553... = $ **55 m (to 2 s.f.)**

> Where v_h is the horizontal velocity, and s_h is the horizontal distance travelled (rather than the height fallen).

It's **Slightly Trickier** if it **Starts Off** at an **Angle**

1) Forces can be in **any direction**, so they're not always at right angles to each other. This is sometimes a bit **awkward** for **calculations**.

2) If something's projected at an **angle** (like, say, a javelin) you start off with both **horizontal** and **vertical velocity**:

Method: 1) **Resolve** the initial velocity into horizontal and vertical components (see below).

2) Use the vertical component to work out **how long** it's in the air and/or **how high** it goes.

3) Use the horizontal component to work out **how far** it goes while it's in the air.

Resolving a **Velocity** means **Splitting** it into **Components**

> You'll also find examples of resolving on p.15, p.30 and p.52.

Example: A box is pushed at a velocity of 10 ms^{-1} at an angle of 0.52 radians above the horizontal. Find the vertical and horizontal components of the velocity.

(diagram: 10 ms^{-1} at 0.52 rad above horizontal, v_V vertical, v_H horizontal)

Use these formulas when resolving velocities:

$$\frac{v_H}{v} = \cos\theta \quad or \quad v_H = v\cos\theta \quad \text{And} \quad \frac{v_V}{v} = \sin\theta \quad or \quad v_V = v\sin\theta$$

Remember that θ is the angle from the **horizontal**.

$v_H = 10 \times \cos(0.52) = 8.67... = $ **8.7 ms^{-1} (to 2 s.f.)**

$v_V = 10 \times \sin(0.52) = 4.96... = $ **5.0 ms^{-1} (to 2 s.f.)**

> To convert from degrees to radians (rad), multiply by $\pi/180°$.
> To convert from radians to degrees, multiply by $180°/\pi$.

Projectile Motion

Time for a **Resolving Example**

Example: An athlete throws a javelin from a height of 1.8 m with a velocity of 21 ms⁻¹ at an upward angle of 45° to the ground. How far is the javelin thrown? Assume the javelin acts as a particle, the ground is horizontal and there is no air resistance.

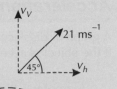

1) Draw a quick sketch of the information given in the question.

2) Start by resolving the velocity into horizontal and vertical components:
$u_h = \cos 45° \times 21 = 14.84...$ ms⁻¹
$u_v = \sin 45° \times 21 = 14.84...$ ms⁻¹

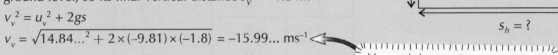

3) Then find how long it's in the air for — start by finding v_v. The javelin starts from a height of 1.8 m and finishes at ground level, so its final vertical distance $s_v = -1.8$ m:

$v_v^2 = u_v^2 + 2gs$
$v_v = \sqrt{14.84...^2 + 2 \times (-9.81) \times (-1.8)} = -15.99...$ ms⁻¹

> You need the negative square root, as this is a velocity towards the ground.

Now you can use this v_v value and $s = \left(\dfrac{u+v}{2}\right)t$ to find the time it stays in the air:

$s_v = \dfrac{(u_v + v_v)}{2} \times t \Rightarrow t = \dfrac{s_v}{(u_v + v_v)} \times 2 = \dfrac{-1.8}{14.84... - 15.99...} \times 2 = 3.144...$ s

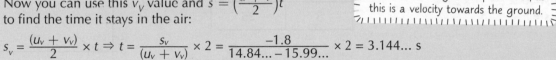

4) Finally, as $a_h = 0$, you can use **speed = distance / time** to work out how far it travels horizontally in this time. The horizontal velocity is just u_h, so:

$s_h = u_h t = 14.84... \times 3.144... = $ **46.7 m (to 3 s.f.)**

Practice Questions

Q1 What is the initial vertical velocity for an object projected horizontally with a velocity of 5 ms⁻¹?

Q2 How does the horizontal velocity of a projectile change with time?

Q3 What is the horizontal component of the velocity of a stone, hurled at 30 ms⁻¹ at 35° to the horizontal.

Exam Questions

Q1 Jason stands on a vertical cliff edge throwing stones into the sea below.
He throws a stone horizontally with a velocity of 20 ms⁻¹, 560 m above sea level.

a) Calculate how long it takes for the stone to hit the water from leaving Jason's hand.
Use $g = 9.81$ ms⁻² and ignore air resistance. [2 marks]

b) Calculate the distance of the stone from the base of the cliff when it hits the water. [2 marks]

Q2 Robin fires an arrow into the air with a vertical velocity of 30 ms⁻¹, and a horizontal velocity of 20 ms⁻¹, from 1 m above horizontal ground. Choose the correct option which shows the maximum height from the ground (to 2 significant figures) reached by his arrow. Use $g = 9.81$ ms⁻² and ignore air resistance. [1 mark]

A	45 m	C	47 m
B	46 m	D	48 m

All this physics makes me want to create projectile motions...

...by throwing my revision books out of the window. The maths on this page can be tricky, but take it step by step and all will be fine. On the plus side, the next page is full of lovely graphs. Who doesn't love a good graph?

Displacement-Time Graphs

Drawing graphs by hand — oh joy. You'd think examiners had never heard of the graphical calculator.
Ah well, until they manage to drag themselves out of the Dark Ages, you'll just have to grit your teeth and get on with it.

Acceleration Means a Curved Displacement-Time Graph

A graph of displacement against time for an **accelerating object** always produces a **curve**.
If the object is accelerating at a **uniform rate**, then the **rate of change** of the **gradient** will be constant.

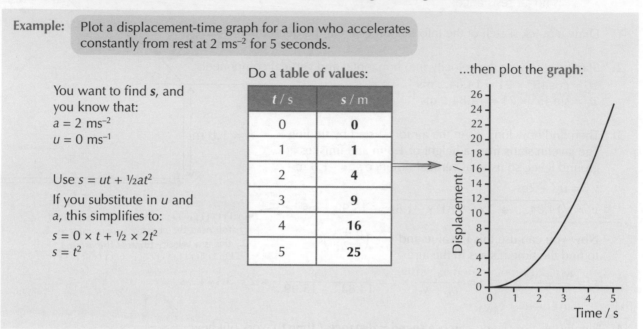

Example: Plot a displacement-time graph for a lion who accelerates constantly from rest at 2 ms^{-2} for 5 seconds.

You want to find s, and you know that:
$a = 2$ ms^{-2}
$u = 0$ ms^{-1}

Use $s = ut + \frac{1}{2}at^2$

If you substitute in u and a, this simplifies to:
$s = 0 \times t + \frac{1}{2} \times 2t^2$
$s = t^2$

Do a **table of values:**

t / s	s / m
0	0
1	1
2	4
3	9
4	16
5	25

...then plot the **graph:**

Different Accelerations Have Different Gradients

In the example above, if the lion has a **different acceleration** it'll change the **gradient** of the curve like this:

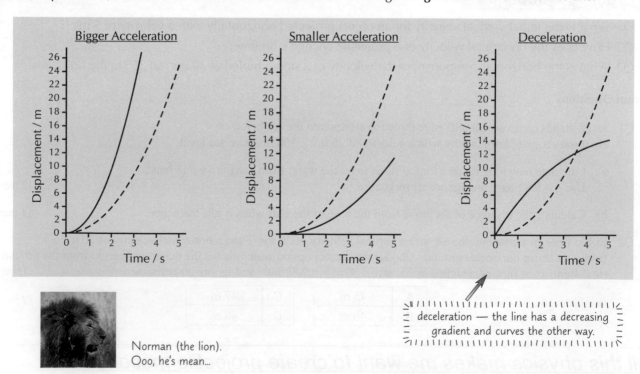

Bigger Acceleration

Smaller Acceleration

Deceleration

Norman (the lion).
Ooo, he's mean...

deceleration — the line has a decreasing
gradient and curves the other way.

Displacement-Time Graphs

The *Gradient* of a *Displacement-Time Graph* Tells You the Velocity

When the velocity is constant, the graph's a **straight line**.
Velocity is defined as...

$$\text{velocity} = \frac{\text{change in displacement}}{\text{change in time}}$$

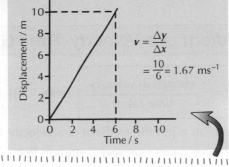

On the graph, this is $\frac{\text{change in } y \ (\Delta y)}{\text{change in } x \ (\Delta x)}$, i.e. the gradient.

So to get the velocity from a displacement-time graph, just find the gradient.

It's the Same with *Curved Graphs*

If the gradient **isn't constant** (i.e. if it's a curved line), it means the object is **accelerating**.

To find the **instantaneous velocity** at a certain point you need to draw a **tangent** to the curve at that point and find its gradient.

To find the **average velocity** over a period of time, just divide the final (change in) displacement by the final (change in) time — it doesn't matter if the graph is curved or not.

Acceleration is $\frac{\text{change in velocity } (\Delta v)}{\text{change in time } (\Delta t)}$, so it is the rate of change of this gradient. If the gradient is constant (straight line) then there is no acceleration, and if it's changing (curved line) then there's acceleration or deceleration.

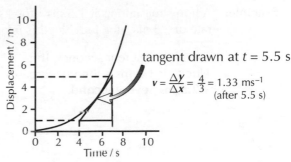

tangent drawn at t = 5.5 s

$v = \frac{\Delta y}{\Delta x} = \frac{4}{3} = 1.33 \text{ ms}^{-1}$
(after 5.5 s)

Practice Questions

Q1 What is given by the slope of a displacement-time graph?
Q2 Sketch a displacement-time graph to show: a) constant velocity,   b) acceleration,   c) deceleration

Exam Questions

Q1 Describe the motion of the cyclist as shown by the graph below. [4 marks]

Q2 A baby crawls 5 m in 8 seconds at a constant velocity. She then rests for 5 seconds before crawling a further 3 m in 5 seconds. Finally, she makes her way back to her starting point in 10 seconds, travelling at a constant speed all the way.

a) Draw a displacement-time graph to show the baby's journey. [4 marks]

b) Calculate her velocity at all the different stages of her journey. [2 marks]

Be ahead of the curve, get to grips with this stuff now...

Whether it's a straight line or a curve, the steeper it is, the greater the velocity. There's nothing difficult about these graphs — the problem is that it's easy to confuse them with velocity-time graphs (next page). If in doubt, think about the gradient — is it velocity or acceleration, is it changing (curve), is it constant (straight line), is it 0 (horizontal line)...

Velocity-Time Graphs

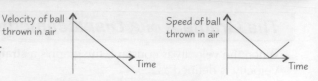

Speed-time graphs and velocity-time graphs are pretty similar. The big difference is that velocity-time graphs can have a negative part to show something travelling in the opposite direction:

The **Gradient** of a **Velocity-Time Graph** tells you the **Acceleration**

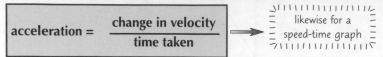

$$\text{acceleration} = \frac{\text{change in velocity}}{\text{time taken}}$$

likewise for a speed-time graph

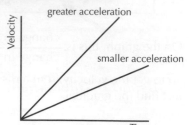

So the acceleration is just the **gradient** of a **velocity-time graph**.

1) **Uniform** acceleration is always a **straight line**.
2) The **steeper** the gradient, the **greater** the acceleration.

When the **acceleration** is **constant**, you get a **straight-line** *v-t* graph. The equation for a straight line is $y = mx + c$. You can rearrange the acceleration equation into the same form, getting $v = u + at$. So on a linear *v-t* graph, **acceleration**, *a*, is the **gradient** (*m*) and the **initial speed**, *u*, is the **y-intercept** (*c*).

Example: A lion strolls along at 1.5 ms⁻¹ for 4 s and then accelerates uniformly at a rate of 2.5 ms⁻² for 4 s. Plot this information on a velocity-time graph.

So, for the first four seconds, the velocity is 1.5 ms⁻¹, then it increases by **2.5 ms⁻¹ every second**:

t (s)	v (ms⁻¹)
0 – 4	1.5
5	4.0
6	6.5
7	9.0
8	11.5

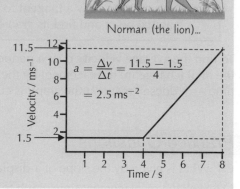

Norman (the lion)...

$$a = \frac{\Delta v}{\Delta t} = \frac{11.5 - 1.5}{4}$$
$$= 2.5 \text{ ms}^{-2}$$

You can see that the **gradient of the line** is **constant** between 4 s and 8 s and has a value of 2.5 ms⁻², representing the **acceleration of the lion**.

Displacement = **Area** under **Velocity-Time Graph**

You know that:

distance travelled = average speed × time

Similarly, the area under a speed-time graph is the total distance travelled.

The **area** under a velocity-time graph tells you the **displacement** of an object. Areas under any **negative** parts of the graph count as negative areas, as they show the object moving **back** to its **start point**.

Example: A racing car on a straight track accelerates uniformly from rest to 40 ms⁻¹ in 10 s. It maintains this speed for a further 20 s before coming to rest by decelerating at a constant rate over the next 15 s. Draw a velocity-time graph for this journey and use it to calculate the total displacement of the racing car.

Split the **graph** up into **sections**: A, B and C
Calculate the **area** of each and **add** the three results together.
A: Area = ½ base × height = ½ × 10 × 40 = 200 m
B: Area = $b × h$ = 20 × 40 = 800 m
C: Area = ½ $b × h$ = ½ × 15 × 40 = 300 m
Total displacement = 1300 m

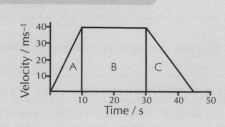

Velocity-Time Graphs

Non-Uniform Acceleration is a Curve on a V-T Graph

1) If the acceleration is changing, the gradient of the velocity-time graph will also be changing — so you **won't** get a **straight line**.

2) **Increasing acceleration** is shown by an **increasing gradient** — like in curve ①.

3) **Decreasing acceleration** is shown by a **decreasing gradient** — like in curve ②.

Simple enough...

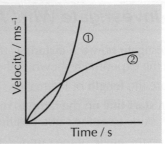

To Find Displacement from a Curved V-T Graph You Estimate the Area

As our velocity-time graph is no longer a simple straight line, we have to use methods to **estimate** the area under the curve. If the graph is on **squared paper**, an easy way to do this is just **count** the squares under the curve. Another way is to split the curve up into **trapeziums**, calculate the **area** of each one and then **add** them all up.

Example: A car decreases its acceleration as it approaches 15 ms^{-1}. Estimate its displacement between 0 and 3 seconds from the velocity-time graph.

Split the area under the curve up into trapeziums and a triangle.

0-1 s — estimate the area with a triangle.
The height of the triangle is 4. $A = \frac{1}{2}(1 \times 4) = 2\,\text{m}$
The base of the triangle is 1.

1-2 s — estimate the area using a trapezium.   Area $= \frac{1}{2}(a + b)h$
a is the length of the first side, $a = 4$
b is the length of the second side, $b = 7$ $A = \frac{1}{2}(4 + 7) \times 1 = 5.5\,\text{m}$
h is the width of each strip, so $h = 1$

2-3 s — trapezium, $a = 7$, $b = 9$, $h = 1$ $A = \frac{1}{2}(7 + 9) \times 1 = 8\,\text{m}$

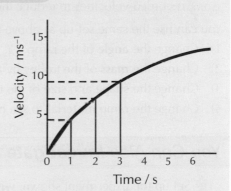

Now add the areas together — Total area = 2 + 5.5 + 8 = 15.5 m
The estimated overall displacement of the car is 15.5 m = **16 m (to 2 s.f.)**

Practice Questions

Q1 How do you calculate acceleration from a velocity-time graph?

Q2 How do you calculate the distance travelled from a speed-time graph?

Q3 Sketch velocity-time graphs for constant velocity and constant acceleration.

Q4 Three trapeziums are drawn side by side under a curve on a *v-t* graph to estimate the area. They have equal widths of 2 s, and side lengths of 1, 3, 7 and 9 ms^{-1}. Show that the displacement for this period is about 30 m.

Exam Question

Q1 A skier accelerates uniformly from rest at 2 ms^{-2} down a straight slope.

a) Sketch a velocity-time graph for the first 5 s of his journey. [2 marks]

b) Use a constant acceleration equation to calculate his displacement at $t = 1, 2, 3, 4$ and 5 s, and plot this information onto a displacement-time graph. [4 marks]

c) Suggest another method of calculating the skier's distance travelled after each second and use this to check your answers to part b). [2 marks]

Still awake — I'll give you five more minutes...

There's a lovely sunset outside my window. It's one of those ones that makes the whole landscape go pinky-yellowish. And that's about as much interest as I can muster on this topic. Normal service will be resumed on page 26, I hope.

Motion Experiments and Stopping Distances

It's all getting a bit hi-tech now — using light gates and video cameras to look at how an object's velocity changes as it rolls down a ramp or crashes into something. Who doesn't love a good motion experiment...

You Can **Investigate** What **Affects** the **Motion** of a Trolley on a Slope

1) To investigate how the **distance** a trolley has rolled affects its speed, set up the experiment shown in the diagram.

2) Measure the **length** of the trolley.

3) Mark a **start line** on the ramp to make sure the trolley always starts from the **same position**.

4) Measure the **angle** of the ramp, θ, and the **distance** from the chosen **start line** to the **light gate**, d.

5) Place the trolley on the **ramp** and **line it up** with the start line. Let go of it so its **initial velocity**, u, is **0**.

6) The **data logger** will record the **time** taken for the trolley to pass through the light gate and calculate the **velocity** of the trolley as it passes through the gate.

7) Change the **starting position** of the trolley, so d is varied.

8) **Repeat** this experiment for each distance 3 times and average the recorded velocities to reduce the **error** in your final result.

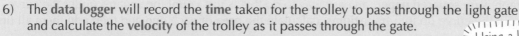

Using a light gate gives a much lower uncertainty in the measurement than using a stopwatch and calculating the velocity manually.

You can use the same set-up as above to investigate other factors. Keep d the same and:

1) Change the **angle** of the ramp.

2) Change the **mass** of the trolley by adding weights to it.

3) Change the **shape** and **size** of the trolley.

4) Change the ramp **material** to see how **friction** affects motion.

Remember to keep all other factors the same whilst you test each of these conditions.

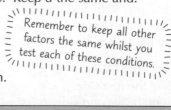
After trolleys the next step is goats.

You Can Also **Investigate** How **Collisions** Affect the **Motion** of a Trolley

1) Set up the experiment shown, with a **video camera** to record the experiment side-on (perpendicular to the trolley's direction of travel).

2) Measure the **length** of the trolley.

3) Turn on the video camera and start **recording**.

4) Place the trolley on the ramp and **line it up** with the start line. Let go of it so its **initial velocity**, u, is **0**.

5) Once the trolley has hit the wall and is at **rest**, stop recording.

You can also investigate what affects the final velocities of **two** trolleys colliding.

1) Set up the experiment shown in the diagram below, with a **video camera** positioned side-on to the motion of the trolleys.

2) Measure the **lengths** of both trolleys.

3) Turn on the video camera and **start recording**.

4) **Push** one trolley so it hits the second trolley.

5) When both trolleys have come to a stop, stop recording.

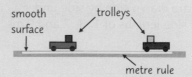

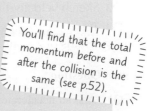
You'll find that the total momentum before and after the collision is the same (see p.52).

1) You can use both of these experiment set-ups to investigate how the **mass** and **velocity** of a trolley (or trolleys) just **before** a collision **affect** the **velocity** (or velocities) after the **collision**.

2) Using **video analysis** software, you can view your videos **frame by frame**. Pick a **point of reference** on the metre stick and count how many **frames** it takes a trolley to pass that point.

3) By knowing how many **frames per second** the video is shot at (the frame rate of the video), you can calculate the **time taken** (t) for the whole trolley to pass that point. You should have recorded the **length** (l) of the trolley, and so you can calculate its **velocity**.

$$\text{Time taken for the trolley to pass the point} = \text{Number of frames for a trolley to pass the point} \times \frac{1\,\text{second}}{\text{Frame rate of camera}}$$

$$\text{velocity} = \frac{l}{t}$$

Motion Experiments and Stopping Distances

From crashing trolleys into each other to trying to avoid crashing a car. There are lots of different factors that affect how quickly a car can stop — the biggest one being its initial velocity.

Many Factors Affect How Quickly a Vehicle Stops

The braking distance and thinking distance together make the **total distance you need to stop** after you see a problem:

> **Thinking distance + Braking distance = Stopping distance**

1) The **reaction time** is the time your body takes to **react** and **hit** the brakes after seeing a hazard.

2) The **thinking distance** is the distance the vehicle travels during the driver's **reaction time**.

3) The **braking distance** is the distance the vehicle travels after the **brakes are applied** until it comes to a complete **stop**.

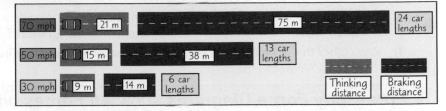

There are many factors which can affect both the **thinking** and **braking** distances:

Thinking distance = speed × reaction time	**Braking distance** depends on the **braking force**, **friction** between the tyres and the road, the **mass** and the **speed**.
Reaction time is increased by:	
1) **Tiredness**.	1) **Braking force** is reduced by **reduced friction** between the brakes and the wheels (**worn** or **badly adjusted brakes**).
2) **Alcohol** or other **drug** use.	2) **Friction** between the tyres and the road is reduced by **wet** or **icy** roads, **leaves or dirt** on the road, **worn-out tyre treads**, etc.
3) **Illness**.	
4) **Distractions** such as noisy children and loud music.	3) **Mass** is affected by the size of the car and what you put in it.

Practice Questions

Q1 Describe an experiment to determine how the masses and velocities of two objects affect their final velocities after a collision.

Q2 Name a factor which affects thinking distance.

Q3 Name a factor which affects braking distance.

Q4 What is the formula for calculating stopping distance?

Exam Questions

Q1 Sarah sees a cow step into the road 30 m ahead of her. Sarah's reaction time is 0.5 s. She is travelling at 20 ms^{-1}. Her maximum braking force is 10 000 N and her car (with her in it) has a mass of 850 kg.

   a) How far does she travel before applying her brakes?   [2 marks]

   b) Calculate Sarah's braking distance. Assume she applies the maximum braking force until she stops.   [3 marks]

   c) Does Sarah hit the cow? Justify your answer with a suitable calculation.   [1 mark]

Q2 Joey is using a light gate and a ramp to investigate how the motion of a toy car can be changed.

   a) Explain how using a ramp with a rougher surface would change Joey's results.   [2 marks]

   b) State another variable you could investigate using the experiment set-up. Explain what effect changing this variable would have on the motion of the car.   [2 marks]

...Huh?... Slow reaction time... Don't know what you mean...

Being safe in a car is mainly common sense — don't drive if you're ill, drunk or just tired, and don't drive a car with dodgy brakes. But you still have to do exam questions, so don't go on till you're sure you know this all by heart.

Forces and Acceleration

You did most of this at GCSE, but that doesn't mean you can just skip over it now. Don't miss out on easy marks...

A **Force** is Needed to **Start**, **Stop**, **Accelerate** or **Decelerate**

1) A **net** (or **resultant**) **force** is needed for an object to **accelerate** (start or stop moving, or change velocity). There is a net force when the forces acting on an object are **not balanced**.

This is known as Newton's First Law — see p.54.

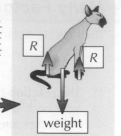

2) If the **forces** acting on a body are **balanced**, it is in **equilibrium** (i.e. not accelerating).

3) For example, the cat in the diagram is in equilibrium because its weight is **exactly balanced** by the two reaction forces from the ground (*R*).

4) Remember that **acceleration** could mean a **change** in **speed** or **direction**, or **both**.

Free-Body Force Diagrams show **All Forces** on a **Single Body**

1) The best way to work out if there is a **net force** is to draw a **free-body force diagram**.

2) **Free-body force** diagrams show a **single body** on its own.

3) The diagram should include all the **forces** that **act on** the body, but **not** the **forces it exerts** on the rest of the world.

4) Remember **forces** are **vector quantities** (p.14) so the **size** and **direction** of the forces should be shown.

Drawing free-body force diagrams isn't too hard — you just need practice. Here are a few **examples**:

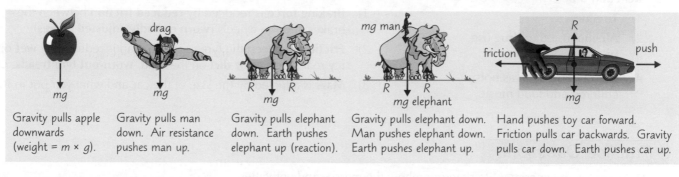

Gravity pulls apple downwards (weight = *m* × *g*).

Gravity pulls man down. Air resistance pushes man up.

Gravity pulls elephant down. Earth pushes elephant up (reaction).

Gravity pulls elephant down. Man pushes elephant down. Earth pushes elephant up.

Hand pushes toy car forward. Friction pulls car backwards. Gravity pulls car down. Earth pushes car up.

You Need to Think About **All** the **Forces** and What **Causes** Them

When working out **force** problems, you have to make sure you've caught **every** force that could be acting on the body. Here's a few examples of **common forces** acting on objects:

1) **Weight** — every object has weight on Earth due to gravity, acting directly downwards (see p.32).

2) **Normal contact force** (or reaction force) — if an object exerts a force on a surface, the surface exerts an equal but opposite force on the object. The force acts normal (perpendicular) to the surface.

3) **Tension** — if a string is pulled tight, tension is the force pulling equally on the objects at either end of the string.

4) **Friction** — if an object is moving, it usually has a friction force acting on it in the opposite direction to motion.

Example — Tension:
Each side pulls on the rope with force 410 N. Tension in the rope balances this force.

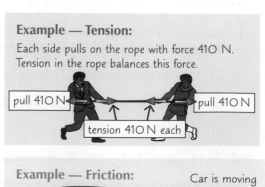

pull 410 N   pull 410 N

tension 410 N each

Examples — Normal Contact Force:

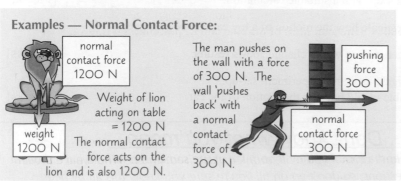

normal contact force 1200 N

weight 1200 N

Weight of lion acting on table = 1200 N
The normal contact force acts on the lion and is also 1200 N.

The man pushes on the wall with a force of 300 N. The wall 'pushes back' with a normal contact force of 300 N.

pushing force 300 N

normal contact force 300 N

Example — Friction:

friction 900 N   driving force 900 N

Car is moving at a constant speed. Driving force is balanced by friction.

Note: These aren't all free-body force diagrams — the forces don't all act on one object.

Forces and Acceleration

Acceleration is Proportional to Force

...which can be written as the well-known equation:

$$\text{net force (N)} = \text{mass (kg)} \times \text{acceleration (ms}^{-2})$$ or $$F = ma$$

From this equation, $1\text{ N} = 1\text{ kg ms}^{-2}$. This is the definition of a newton. $F = ma$ is a special case of Newton's Second Law — see page 54.

Learn this — you won't be given it in your exam.
And learn what it means too:

1) It says that the **more force** you have acting on a certain mass, the **more acceleration** you get.

2) It says that for a given force the **more mass** you have, the **less acceleration** you get.

REMEMBER:
1) The **resultant force** is the **vector sum** of all the forces.
2) The force is **always** measured in **newtons**.
3) The **mass** is always measured in **kilograms**.
4) The **acceleration** is always in the **same direction** as the **resultant force** and is measured in **ms^{-2}**.

Galileo said that All Objects Fall at the Same Rate*

*(if you ignore air resistance)

You can see **why** with a bit of ball dropping and a dash of $F = ma$...

Example: Imagine dropping two balls at the same time — ball **1** being heavy, and ball **2** being light. Then use $F = ma$ to find their acceleration.

mass = m_1 resultant force = F_1 acceleration = a_1

$$F_1 = m_1 a_1$$

Ignoring air resistance, the only force acting on the ball is weight, given by $W_1 = m_1 g$ (where g = gravitational field strength = 9.81 Nkg^{-1} — see p.32).

So: $F_1 = m_1 a_1 = W_1 = m_1 g$

So: $m_1 a_1 = m_1 g$, then m_1 cancels out to give: $a_1 = g$

mass = m_2 resultant force = F_2 acceleration = a_2

$$F_2 = m_2 a_2$$

Ignoring air resistance, the only force acting on the ball is weight, given by $W_2 = m_2 g$ (where g = gravitational field strength = 9.81 Nkg^{-1}).

So: $F_2 = m_2 a_2 = W_2 = m_2 g$

So: $m_2 a_2 = m_2 g$, then m_2 cancels out to give: $a_2 = g$

... in other words, the **acceleration** is **independent of the mass**. It makes **no difference** whether the ball is **heavy or light**. And I've kindly **hammered home the point** by showing you two almost identical examples.

Practice Questions

Q1 Sketch a free-body force diagram for an ice hockey puck moving across the ice (assuming no friction).

Q2 Give an example of: a) a tension force,   b) a normal contact force.

Q3 Write down the equation that links mass, force and acceleration, and explain what it means for a given mass.

Q4 Ball A has a mass of 5 kg and ball B has a mass of 3 kg. Both balls are dropped from the same height at the same time — which one hits the ground first? Why?

Exam Questions

Q1 Draw labelled free-body force diagrams to show the forces acting on a parachutist:

a) accelerating downwards. [1 mark]

b) falling at a constant speed. [1 mark]

Q2 A boat is being driven with a constant force of 500 N in the direction of motion. It experience a drag force of 300 N from the water and air resistance of 100 N. The total mass of the boat and its passengers is 250 kg.

a) Calculate the magnitude of the net force acting on the boat at this point in time. [1 mark]

b) Calculate the magnitude of the acceleration of the boat at this point in time. [1 mark]

\<body\> Force diagram, one careful owner, free to good home... \</body\>

So there you have it — if you drop a cannonball and a football, they'll both fall at the same rate. Who'd have thought they were so similar. This is all pretty straightforward — make sure you know it, don't slip up on the simple stuff.

Forces and Equilibrium

Remember the vector stuff from pages 14-15...? Good, you're going to need it...

Resolving a Force means Splitting it into Components

1) **Forces** are **vector quantities** and so when you draw the forces on an object, the **arrow labels** should show the **size** and **direction** of the forces.

2) Forces can be in **any direction**, so they're not always at right angles to each other. This is sometimes a bit **awkward** for **calculations**.

3) To make an 'awkward' force easier to deal with, you can think of it as **two separate forces**, acting at **right angles** to **each other**.

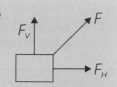

The force **F** has exactly the same effect as the horizontal and vertical forces, F_H and F_V.

Replacing **F** with F_H and F_V is called **resolving the force F**.

4) To find the size of a component force in a particular direction, you need to use **trigonometry**. Forces are vectors, so you treat them in the same way as velocities — put them end to end.

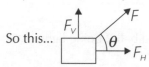

So this... ...could be drawn like this:

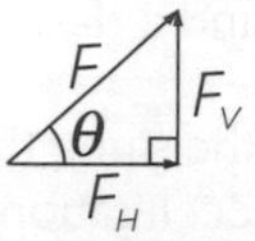

Using trig. you get:

$$\frac{F_H}{F} = \cos\theta \quad \text{or} \quad F_H = F\cos\theta$$

And:

$$\frac{F_V}{F} = \sin\theta \quad \text{or} \quad F_V = F\sin\theta$$

Remember 'SOH CAH TOA' for right-angle triangles.

Example:

A tree trunk is pulled along the ground by an elephant exerting a force of 1200 N at an angle of 25° to the horizontal. Calculate the components of this force in the horizontal and vertical directions.

Horizontal force = 1200 × cos 25° = **1090 N (to 3 s.f.)**

Vertical force = 1200 × sin 25° = **507 N (to 3 s.f.)**

Three Forces Acting on a Point in Equilibrium form a Triangle

1) When **three** coplanar (all in the same plane) forces all act on an object in **equilibrium**, you know there is **no net force** on the object — the sum of the forces is zero.

$$F_1 + F_2 + F_3 = 0$$

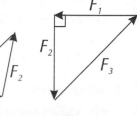

2) You can draw the forces as a triangle, forming a **closed loop** like these:

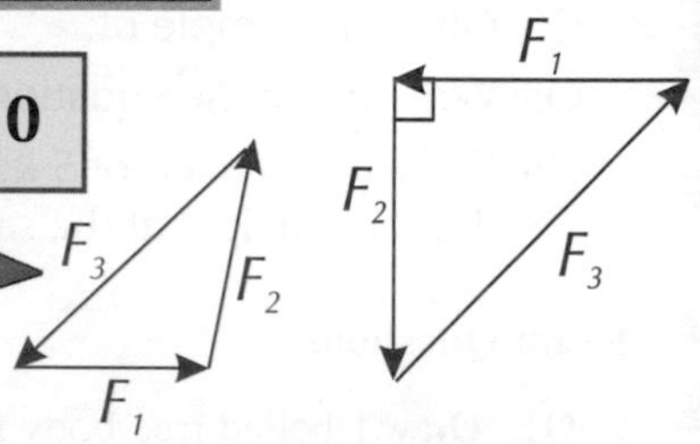

3) Be careful when you draw the triangles not to go into autopilot and draw F_3 as the sum of F_1 and F_2 — it has to be in the **opposite** direction to balance the other two forces.

4) You can then use the triangles to while away Saturday nights in with your friends working out the magnitude or direction of a missing force, either by using Pythagoras, or by measuring on a scale diagram (p.14).

The sum of all the angles in a triangle is 180° — you might need to use this to answer exam questions.

Example:

Tim hangs a picture of his brother up using a piece of string. The picture weighs 0.3 N and is in equilibrium, as shown. Find the magnitude of F.

Draw a vector triangle.

Then you need to use **Pythagoras** to find the magnitude of F.

$$F = \sqrt{0.3^2 + 0.4^2} = \sqrt{0.25^2} = \textbf{0.5 N}$$

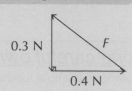

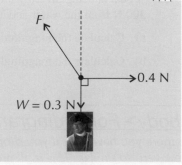

Forces and Equilibrium

You *Add Components Back Together* to get the *Resultant Force*

1) If **two forces** act on an object, you find the **resultant** (net) **force** by adding the **vectors** together and creating a **closed triangle**, with the resultant force represented by the **third side**.

2) Forces are vectors (as you know), so you use **vector addition** — draw the forces as vector arrows put 'tip-to-tail'.

3) Then it's yet more trigonometry to find the **angle** and the **length** of the third side.

Example: Two dung beetles roll a dung ball along the ground at constant velocity. Beetle A applies a force of 0.5 N northwards, beetle B exerts a force of 0.2 N eastwards. Find the resultant force on the dung ball.

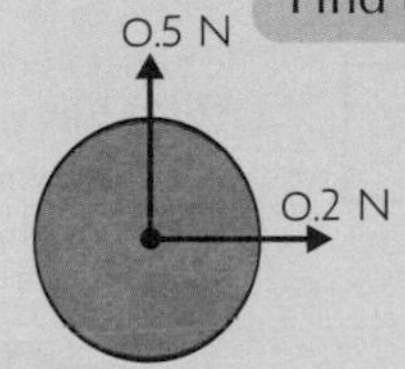

Draw a triangle:

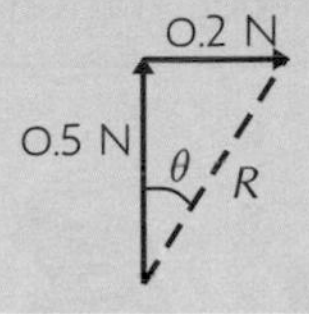

By Pythagoras, $R^2 = 0.5^2 + 0.2^2$, so $R = \sqrt{0.29} = 0.54$ N (to 2 s.f.)

$\tan\theta = \frac{0.2}{0.5}$ so $\theta = \tan^{-1}0.4 = 22°$ (to 2 s.f.)

So the resultant force is **0.54 N** at an angle of **22°** from north.

Choose sensible *Axes* for *Resolving*

Use directions that **make sense** for the situation you're dealing with. If you've got an object on a slope, choose your directions **along the slope** and **at right angles to it**. You can turn the paper to an angle if that helps.

Examiners like to call a slope an "inclined plane".

Always choose sensible axes

Example:

Jemima's bone
2.5 N (to 2 s.f.) slope
30° 30°
4.3 N (to 2 s.f.)
5 N weight

The component of the bone's weight down the slope is 2.5 N so you'd need 2.5 N of friction to stop it sliding away.

Practice Questions

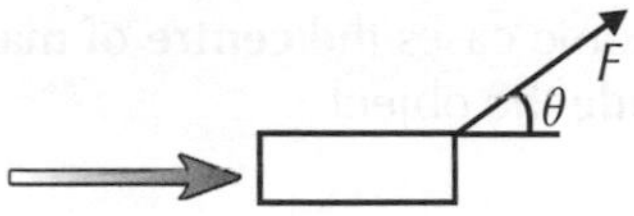

Q1 What are the horizontal and vertical components of the force *F*?

Q2 How could you use a scale drawing to show that three coplanar forces are producing no net force?

Q3 Three forces act on an object in equilibrium. What is the sum of the forces?

Exam Questions

Q1 A picture is suspended from a hook as shown in the diagram. Calculate the tension force, *T*, in the string.

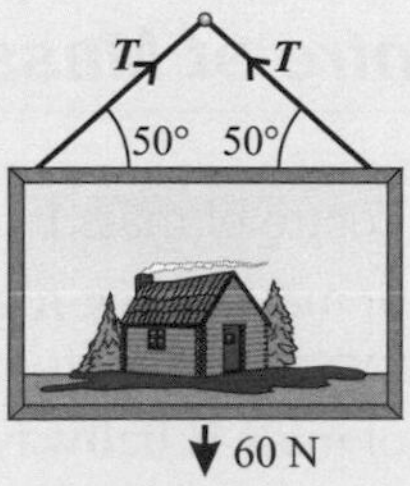

T   *T*
50° 50°
↓ 60 N
[2 marks]

Q2 Two elephants pull a tree trunk as shown in the diagram. Calculate the resultant force on the tree trunk.

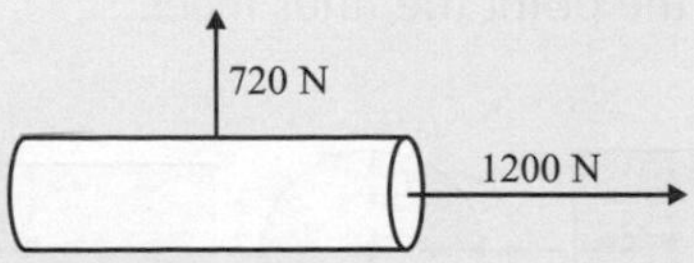

720 N
1200 N
[2 marks]

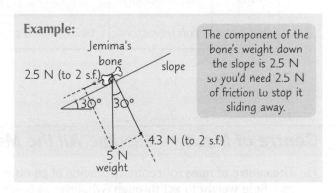

I'm in e-quill-ibrium — if I lose my pen, I always order a new one right away...

Remember those $F\cos\theta$ and $F\sin\theta$ bits. Write them on bits of paper and stick them to your wall. Scrawl them on your pillow. Tattoo them on your brain. Whatever it takes — you just have to learn them.

Mass, Weight and Centre of Mass

I'm sure you know all this 'mass', 'weight' and 'centre of mass' stuff from GCSE. But let's just make sure...

The Mass of a Body makes it Resist Changes in Motion

1) The **mass** of an object is the **amount of 'stuff'** (or **matter**) in it. It's measured in **kg**.

2) The greater an object's mass, the greater its **resistance** to a **change in velocity** (called its **inertia**).

3) The **mass** of an object **doesn't change** if the strength of the **gravitational field** changes.

4) Weight is a **force**. It's measured in **newtons** (N), like all forces.

5) Weight is the **force experienced by a mass** due to a **gravitational field**.

6) The weight of an object **does vary** according to the size of the **gravitational field** acting on it.

> **weight = mass × gravitational field strength** ($W = mg$) where g = 9.81 Nkg^{-1} on Earth.

Learn this equation — you won't be given it in the exam.

This table shows Gerald (the lion*)'s mass and weight on the Earth and the Moon.

Name	Quantity	Earth (g = 9.81 Nkg^{-1})	Moon (g = 1.6 Nkg^{-1})
Mass	Mass (scalar)	150 kg	150 kg
Weight	Force (vector)	1470 N (to 3 s.f.)	240 N (to 2 s.f.)

Weight 240 N

Weight 1470 N

Centre of Mass — Assume All the Mass is in One Place

1) The **centre of mass** (or centre of gravity) of an object is the **single point** that you can consider its **whole weight** to **act through** (whatever its orientation).

2) The object will always **balance** around this **point**, although in some cases the **centre of mass** will **fall outside** the object.

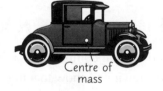

Centre of mass

Centre of mass

Centre of mass

Find the Centre of Mass either by Symmetry...

1) To find the centre of mass in for a **regular** object you can just use **symmetry**.

2) The centre of mass of any regular shape is at its **centre** — where the lines of symmetry will cross.

3) The centre of mass is **halfway** through the **thickness** of the object at the point the lines meet.

The symmetry in this picture shows the centre of cuteness.

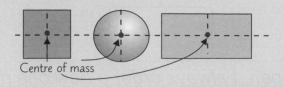

Centre of mass

*Yes, I know — I just like lions, OK...

Mass, Weight and Centre of Mass

... Or By Experiment

Experiment to find the Centre of Mass of an Irregular Object

1) **Hang** the object freely from a point (e.g. one corner).
2) Draw a **vertical line** downwards from the point of suspension — use a plumb bob to get your line exactly vertical.
3) Hang the object from a different point.
4) Draw another vertical line down.
5) The centre of mass is where the two lines **cross**.

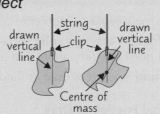

A plumb bob is just a weight on a string — when suspended, the string will be exactly vertical.

How High the Centre of Mass is tells you How Stable the Object is

1) An object will be nice and **stable** if it has a **low centre** of **mass** and a **wide base area**. This idea is used a lot in design, e.g. racing cars.

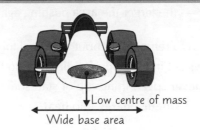

Low centre of mass
Wide base area

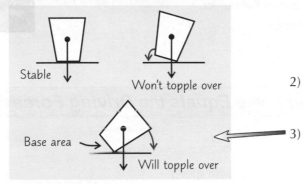

Stable

Won't topple over

Base area

Will topple over

2) The **higher** the **centre of mass**, and the **smaller** the **base area**, the **less stable** the object will be. Think of unicyclists...

3) An object will topple over if a **vertical line** drawn **downwards** from its **centre of mass** falls **outside** its **base area**. This is because of the moments about the pivot — see p.38.

Practice Questions

Q1 A lioness has a mass of 200 kg. What would be her mass and weight on Earth and on the Moon (where $g = 1.6 \, \text{Nkg}^{-1}$)?

Q2 Define centre of mass.

Exam Questions

Q1 Joanne weighs X N on Earth. Which of the following statements are correct?

A She will weigh the same on the Moon as on Earth.

B Her mass is equal to $\frac{X}{g}$ kg.

C Her mass depends on the gravitational field strength.

D Her acceleration due to gravity will be the same on Earth as the Moon. [1 mark]

Q2 a) Describe an experiment to find the centre of mass of an object of uniform density with a constant thickness and irregular cross-section. [3 marks]

b) Identify one major source of uncertainty and suggest a way to reduce its effect on the precision of the result. [2 marks]

The centre of mass of this book should be round about page 55...

This is a really useful area of physics. To would-be nuclear physicists it might seem a little dull, but if you want to be an engineer — something a bit more useful (no offence Einstein) — then things like centre of mass and weight are dead important things to understand. You know, for designing things like cars and submarines... yep, pretty useful I'd say.

Drag and Terminal Velocity

If you jump out of a plane at 2000 metres, you want to know that you're not going to be accelerating all the way.

Friction is a Force that Opposes Motion

There are two main types of friction:

1) **Contact friction** between **solid surfaces** (which is what we usually mean when we just use the word 'friction'). You don't need to worry about that too much for now.

2) **Fluid friction** (known as **drag** or fluid resistance or air resistance).

> **Fluid Friction or Drag**:
>
> 1) 'Fluid' is a word that means either a **liquid or a gas** — something that can **flow**.
> 2) The force depends on the thickness (or **viscosity**) of the fluid.
> 3) It **increases** as the **speed increases** (for simple situations it's directly proportional, but you don't need to worry about the mathematical relationship).
> 4) It also depends on the **shape** and **size** of the object moving through it — the larger the **area** pushing against the fluid, the greater the resistance force.

Things you need to remember about frictional forces:

1) They **always** act in the **opposite direction** to the **motion** of the object.
2) They can **never** speed things up or start something moving.
3) They convert **kinetic energy** into **heat**.

Terminal Velocity — when the Friction Force Equals the Driving Force

You will reach a **terminal velocity** at some point, if you have:

1) a **driving force** that stays the **same** all the time
2) a **frictional** or **drag force** (or collection of forces) that increases with speed

There are **three main stages** to reaching terminal velocity:

The car **accelerates** from **rest** using a constant driving force.

As the **velocity increases**, the **resistance forces increase** (because of things like turbulence — you don't need the details). This **reduces the resultant force** on the car and hence **reduces its acceleration**.

Eventually the car reaches a velocity at which the **resistance forces are equal to the driving force**. There is now **no resultant force** and **no acceleration**, so the car carries on at **constant velocity**.

Sketching a Graph for Terminal Velocity

You need to be able to **recognise** and **sketch** the graphs for **velocity against time** and **acceleration against time** for the **terminal velocity** situation.

Nothing for it but practice — shut the book and sketch them from memory. Keep doing it till you get them right every time.

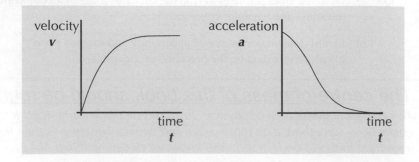

Drag and Terminal Velocity

Things *Falling* through *Air* or *Water* Reach a *Terminal Velocity* too

When something's falling through air, the weight of the object is a **constant** force accelerating the object downwards. Air resistance is a frictional force opposing this motion, which **increases** with **speed**.

So before a parachutist opens the parachute, exactly the same thing happens as with the car example:

1) A skydiver leaves a plane and will **accelerate** until the **air resistance** equals his **weight**.

2) He will then be travelling at a **terminal velocity**.

But... the terminal velocity of a person in free fall is too great to land without dying a horrible death. The **parachute increases** the **air resistance massively**, which slows him down to a lower terminal velocity:

3) Before reaching the ground he will **open his parachute**, which immediately **increases the air resistance** so it is now **bigger** than his **weight**.

4) This **slows him down** until his speed has dropped enough for the **air resistance** to be **equal to his weight** again. This new terminal velocity is small enough to survive landing.

The *v-t* graph is a bit different, because you have a new terminal velocity being reached after the parachute is opened:

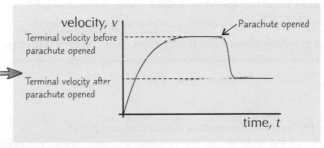

Measure the Terminal Velocity of a Ball Bearing

You can calculate the terminal velocity of a **ball bearing** (a little steel ball) in a **viscous** (thick) liquid by setting up an experiment like this:

You don't have to use elastic bands — you could also use insulation tape or another marker for your intervals.

1) Put **elastic bands** around the tube of viscous liquid at **fixed distances** using a **ruler**.
2) **Drop** a ball bearing into the tube, and use a **stopwatch** to record the time at which it reaches **each band**. Record your results in a **table** (see below).
3) **Repeat** this a few times to reduce the effect of **random errors** on your results. You can use a **strong magnet** to remove the ball bearing from the tube.
4) **Calculate** the times taken by the ball bearing to travel between consecutive elastic bands and calculate an **average** for each reading. Use the **average times** and the **distance between bands** to calculate the **average velocity** between **each pair** of elastic bands.
5) You should find that the average velocity **increases** at first, then **stays constant** — this is the ball bearing's **terminal velocity** in the viscous liquid used.

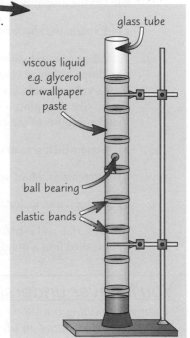

Elastic band	Time / s	Time from last band / s	Average time / s	Average velocity / ms⁻¹
2	1			
	2			
	3			
3	1			
	2			
	3			

If your stopwatch has a lap timer, you might be able to measure these times directly.

Drag and Terminal Velocity

You can Work Out what Affects Terminal Velocity

Prof. Fraise dedicated his life to investigating terminal velocity in fluids.

1) Use your average velocity data to plot a graph of **velocity** against **time**. Draw a smooth curve and use it to estimate the terminal velocity.

2) You might be asked to draw **force diagrams** as the ball bearing falls. Remember that the forces are balanced when the ball reaches terminal velocity.

3) You can change parts of your experiment to see what effect they have on terminal velocity and the time taken to reach terminal velocity. For example you could:

   - Change the **liquid** — the terminal velocity will be **lower** in more viscous (thicker) liquids because the drag is **greater**. Try mixing water into wallpaper paste and see by how much the terminal velocity increases when the drag is lower.

   - Change the **size** of the ball. What happens if the ball is larger? Or smaller?

   - Change the **shape** of the thing you are dropping. The drag force will be greater on **less streamlined** shapes.

   - Change the **mass** of the thing you are dropping, while keeping the **size** the **same** (this might be a bit tricky). You should find that **heavier objects** reach a **faster** terminal velocity because a **greater drag force** is needed to balance the extra weight. (Remember, objects with different masses only fall at the same rate if drag is ignored — p.29.)

Turn back to p.24-25 for more on velocity-time graphs.

Practice Questions

Q1 What forces limit the speed of a skier going down a slope?

Q2 What conditions cause a terminal velocity to be reached?

Q3 Sketch a graph to show how the acceleration changes with time for an object falling through air.

Exam Questions

Q1 A space probe free-falls towards the surface of a planet.
The graph on the right shows the velocity data recorded by the probe as it falls.

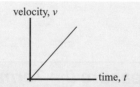

velocity, v

time, t

a) The planet does not have an atmosphere. Explain how you can tell this from the graph. [2 marks]

b) On the graph, sketch the line you would expect to see if the planet did have an atmosphere. [2 marks]

c) Explain the shape of the graph you have drawn. [3 marks]

Q2 A student is investigating how the terminal velocity of paper cones varies with cone size.
She drops weighted cones of base diameter 5 cm, 10 cm and 15 cm point-down from a height of 2 m and uses a video camera and video analysis software to obtain data on the displacement of the cone at certain times. She then plots a displacement-time graph to calculate the terminal velocity. You may assume that the weights of the cones are negligible compared to that of the weights used to stabilise them.

a) State which size of cone you expect to have the lowest terminal velocity. Explain your answer. [2 marks]

b) Sketch a graph of velocity against time for the three cones. Put all three curves on the same axes. [3 marks]

c) Suggest one factor the student must keep the same in her experiment and explain why. [1 mark]

d) Describe and explain how the velocity-time graph would change if the largest cone was crushed into a rough ball shape. [3 marks]

You'll never understand this without going parachuting...*

When you're doing questions about terminal velocity, remember the frictional forces reduce acceleration, not speed. They usually don't slow an object down, apart from in the parachute example, where the skydiver is travelling faster when the parachute opens than the terminal velocity for the parachute-skydiver combination.

* No. 37 in a series of the 100 least convincing excuses for an interesting holiday.

Density, Pressure and Upthrust

Yikes, three whole things on one page. Grab a coffee, take a deep breath and put on your snazziest learning hat...

Density is Mass per Unit Volume

Density is a measure of the '**compactness**' (for want of a better word) of a substance. It relates the **mass** of a substance to how much **space** it takes up.

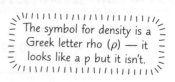
The symbol for density is a Greek letter rho (ρ) — it looks like a p but it isn't.

$$\text{density} = \frac{\text{mass}}{\text{volume}} \qquad \rho = \frac{m}{V}$$

The units of density are g cm^{-3} or kg m^{-3}
$1 \text{ g cm}^{-3} = 1000 \text{ kg m}^{-3}$

1) The density of an object depends on what it's made of. Density **doesn't vary** with **size or shape**.

2) The **average density** of an object determines whether it **floats** or **sinks**.

3) A solid object will **float** on a fluid if it has a **lower density** than the **fluid**.
E.g. The density of iron is 7.9 g cm^{-3} — this is **greater** than the density of water (1 g cm^{-3}) so it will **sink** in water.

Pressure is Force per Unit Area

1) Pressure is the **amount of force** applied per **unit area**. It is measured in pascals (**Pa**), which are equivalent to newtons per square metre (Nm^{-2}).

$$\text{pressure} = \frac{\text{force}}{\text{area}} \qquad p = \frac{F}{A}$$

2) The extra pressure acting on an object due to a fluid depends on the **depth** of the object in the fluid (h), the **density** of the fluid (ρ) and the **acceleration** due to gravity (g).

$$p = h\rho g$$

Bodies in Fluids Experience Upthrust

1) Upthrust is an **upward force** that fluids exert on objects that are **completely** or **partially submerged** in the fluid. It's caused because the top and bottom of a submerged object are at different depths. Since $p = h\rho g$, there is a difference in pressure which causes an overall upwards force known as upthrust.

2) **Archimedes' principle** says that when a body is completely or partially immersed in a fluid, it experiences an **upthrust** equal to the **weight** of the fluid it has **displaced**.

$$\boxed{\text{upthrust} = \text{weight of fluid displaced}}$$

This is just because
$(h_2 - h_1)\rho g A = V\rho g = mg = W$

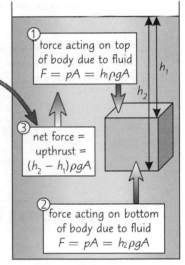
① force acting on top of body due to fluid $F = pA = h_1\rho g A$
③ net force = upthrust = $(h_2 - h_1)\rho g A$
② force acting on bottom of body due to fluid $F = pA = h_2\rho g A$

Example: **Submarines** make use of upthrust to dive underwater and return to the surface. To sink, large tanks are filled with water to **increase** the weight of the submarine so that it **exceeds** the upthrust. To rise to the surface, the tanks are filled with compressed air to **reduce** the weight so that it's **less** than the upthrust.

Practice Questions

Q1 State the equation that gives the pressure on an object due to the density of the fluid it is submerged in.

Q2 State Archimedes' principle.

Exam Questions

Q1 a) A cylinder of aluminium with radius 4 cm and height 6 cm, has a mass of 820 g. Calculate its density. [2 marks]
b) Use the information from part a) to calculate the mass of a cube of aluminium of side 5 cm. [1 mark]

Q2 Calculate the pressure when a force of 17.0 N is applied over a square table top with side length 1.72 m. [2 marks]

Q3 Calculate the pressure due to seawater acting on a point that is 2.4 m below the surface of a sea. Water in the sea has a density of 1024 kg m^{-3}. [1 mark]

Q4 Find the upthrust acting on a ball of radius 5.20 cm submerged in water of density 1050 kg m^{-3}. [3 marks]

Don't be dense — you must learn the thrust of this page (no pressure...)

*You might have met density and pressure before. Perhaps you even invite them around for tea sometimes.
Upthrust combines them and adds in a whole extra layer of fun. Yes, fun. I'll start to believe it if I say it often enough...*

Moments and Torques

This is not a time for jokes. There is not a moment to lose. The time for torquing is over. Oh ho ho ho *bang*. (Ow.)

A **Moment** is the **Turning Effect** of a **Force**

The **moment**, or **torque**, of a **force** depends on the **size** of the force and **how far** the force is applied from the **turning point**:

> **moment of a force (in Nm) = force (in N) × perpendicular distance from pivot (in m)**

In symbols, that's:

$$M = F \times d$$

Moments must be **Balanced** or the **Object** will **Turn**

The **principle of moments** states that for a body to be in **equilibrium**, the **sum of the clockwise moments** about any point **equals** the **sum of the anticlockwise moments** about the same point.

Example: Two children sit on a seesaw as shown in the diagram. An adult balances the seesaw at one end. Calculate the size and direction of the force that the adult needs to apply.

In equilibrium, Σ anticlockwise moments $= \Sigma$ clockwise moments

Σ means "the sum of"

$$400 \times 1.5 = 300 \times 1 + 1.5F$$
$$600 = 300 + 1.5F$$

Final Answer: $F = \textbf{200 N downwards}$

1.5 m   1.0 m   0.5 m

400 N   300 N

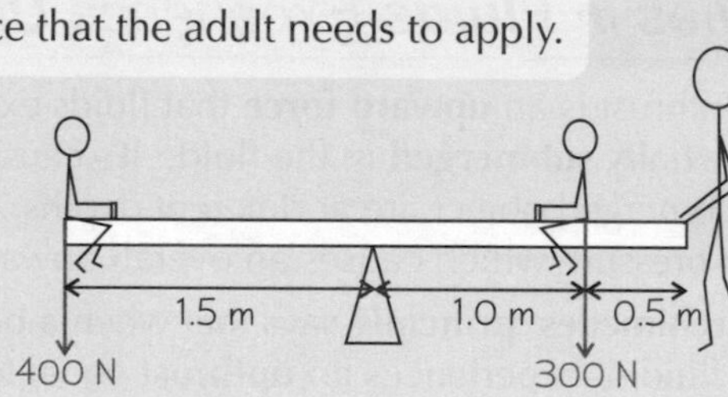

Muscles, **Bones** and **Joints** Act as **Levers**

1) In a lever, an **effort force** acts against a **load force** by means of a **rigid object** rotating around a **pivot**.

2) You can use the **principle of moments** to answer lever questions:

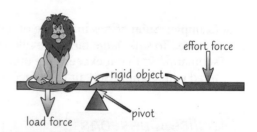

effort force

rigid object

load force   pivot

Example: A bag of gold weighing 100 N is being held still by biceps in a forearm weighing 20 N. Calculate the force *E* exerted by the biceps.

Take moments about **A**.

In equilibrium:

Σ anticlockwise moments $= \Sigma$ clockwise moments

$$(100 \times 0.4) + (20 \times 0.2) = 0.04E$$
$$40 + 4 = 0.04E$$

Final answer: $E = \textbf{1100 N upwards}$

This is a bit of a simplified example — there are actually lots of muscles involved, but the biceps does the majority of the work so it's a good illustration of what's going on.

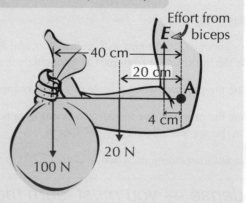

Effort from
E biceps

← 40 cm →

20 cm

A

4 cm

100 N   20 N

Moments and Torques

A *Couple* is a *Pair* of *Forces*

1) A couple is a **pair** of **forces** of **equal size** which act **parallel** to each other, but in **opposite directions**.

2) A couple doesn't cause any resultant linear force, but **does** produce a **turning force** (usually called a **torque** rather than a moment).

The **size** of this **torque** depends on the **size** of the **forces** and the **distance** between them.

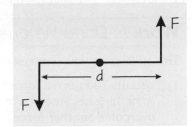

> **Torque of a couple (in Nm) = size of one of the forces (in N) × perpendicular distance between the forces (in m)**

In symbols, that's: $T = F \times d$

Example:

A cyclist turns a sharp right corner by applying equal but opposite forces of 20 N to the ends of the handlebars. The length of the handlebars is 0.6 m. Calculate the torque applied to the handlebars.

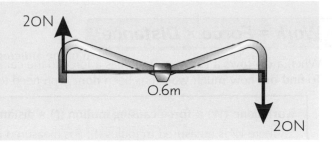

20N

0.6m

20N

Torque = $F \times d = 20 \times 0.6 = $ **12 Nm**

Practice Questions

Q1 A force of 54 N acts at a perpendicular distance of 84 cm from a pivot. Calculate the moment of the force.

Q2 A girl of mass 40 kg sits 1.5 m from the middle of a seesaw.
Show that her brother, mass 50 kg, must sit 1.2 m from the middle if the seesaw is to balance.

Q3 What is meant by the word 'couple'?

Q4 A racing car driver uses both hands to apply equal and opposite forces of 65 N to the edge of a steering wheel with radius 20 cm. Calculate the torque of the forces.

Exam Questions

Q1 A driver is changing his flat tyre. The torque required to undo the nut is 60 Nm. He uses a 0.4 m long double-ended wheel wrench as shown. Calculate the force that he must apply at each end of the wrench.

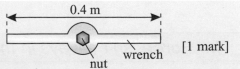

0.4 m

nut

wrench

[1 mark]

Q2 A diver of mass 60 kg stands on the end of a diving board 2 m from the pivot point. Calculate the upward force exerted on the retaining spring 30 cm from the pivot.

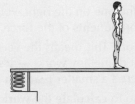

[2 marks]

It's all about balancing — just ask a tightrope walker...

Moments are great. They explain why using wheelbarrows is loads easier (no pun intended) than plain old lifting. And why wrenches are better at unscrewing than fingers. They help us understand why things topple over too — see p.33.

Work and Power

As everyone knows, work in Physics isn't like normal work. It's harder. Work also has a specific meaning that's to do with movement and forces. You'll have seen this at GCSE — it just comes up in more detail here.

Work is Done Whenever Energy is Transferred

This table gives you some examples of **work being done** and the **energy changes** that happen.

1) Usually you need a force to move something because you're having to **overcome another force**.

2) The thing being moved has **kinetic energy** while it's **moving**.

3) The kinetic energy is transferred to **another form of energy** when the movement stops.

ACTIVITY	WORK DONE AGAINST	FINAL ENERGY FORM
Lifting up a box.	gravity	gravitational potential energy
Pushing a chair across a level floor.	friction	heat
Pushing two magnetic north poles together.	magnetic force	magnetic energy
Stretching a spring.	stiffness of spring	elastic potential energy

The word **'work'** in Physics means the **amount of energy transferred** from one form to another when a force causes a movement of some sort. It's measured in **joules** (J).

Work = Force × Distance

When a car tows a caravan, it applies a force to the caravan to move it to where it's wanted. To **find out** how much **work** has been **done**, you need to use the **equation**:

> **work done (W)** = **force causing motion (F)** × **distance moved (x)**, or **W = Fx**
>
> ...where W is measured in joules (J), F is measured in newtons (N) and x is measured in metres (m).

Points to remember:

1) **Work** is the **energy** that's been **changed** from one form to another — it's not necessarily the **total** energy. E.g. moving a book from a low shelf to a higher one will increase its gravitational potential energy, but it had some potential energy to start with.
   Here, the **work done** would be the **increase** in potential energy, **not the total** potential energy.

2) Remember the distance needs to be measured in metres — if you have **distance in centimetres or kilometres**, you need to **convert** it to metres first.

3) The force **F** will be a **fixed** value in any calculations, either because it's **constant** or because it's the **average** force.

4) The equation assumes that the **direction of the force** is the **same** as the **direction of movement**.

5) The equation gives you the **definition** of the joule (symbol J):
   'One joule is the work done when a force of 1 newton moves an object through a distance of 1 metre'.

The Force isn't always in the Same Direction as the Movement

Sometimes the **direction of movement** is **different** from the **direction of the** force.

Example:

1) To **calculate the work done** in a situation like the one on the right, you need to consider the **horizontal** and **vertical components** of the **force**.

2) The only **movement** is in the **horizontal** direction. This means the **vertical force** is not causing any motion (and hence not doing any work) — it's just **balancing** out some of the **weight**, meaning there's a **smaller reaction force**.

direction of force on sledge
rosebud
direction of motion

3) The horizontal force is causing the motion — so to **calculate** the work done, this is the **only force** you need to consider. Which means we get:

$$W = Fx \cos \theta$$

Where θ is the **angle** between the **direction of the force** and the **direction of motion**. See page 30 for more on resolving forces.

F
θ
$F \cos \theta$ ➞ Direction of motion

Work and Power

Power = Work Done per Second

Power means many things in everyday speech, but in physics (of course!) it has a special meaning. Power is the **rate of doing work** — in other words it is the **amount of energy transformed** from one form to another **per second**. You **calculate power** from this equation:

> **Power (P) = work done (W) / time (t)**, or $P = \dfrac{W}{t}$ ...where P is measured in watts (W), W is measured in joules (J) and t is measured in seconds (s).

The **watt** (symbol W) is defined as a **rate of energy transfer** equal to **1 joule per second** (Js^{-1}).

Yep, that's another **equation and definition** for you to **learn**.

> W stands for watts (the unit of power) — don't get it confused with W, work done.

Power is also Force × Velocity (P = Fv)

Sometimes, it's **easier** to use **this version** of the power equation. This is how you get it:

1) You **know** $P = W/t$.
2) You also **know** $W = Fx$, which gives **$P = Fx/t$**.
3) But $v = x/t$, which you can substitute into the above equation to give **$P = Fv$**.
4) It's easier to use this if you're given the **speed** in the question.
   Learn this equation as a **shortcut** to link **power** and **speed**.

> **Example:** A car is travelling at a speed of 10 ms^{-1} and is kept going against the frictional force by a driving force of 500 N in the direction of motion. Find the power supplied by the engine to keep the car moving.
>
> Use the shortcut **$P = Fv$**, which gives:
> $P = 500 \times 10 = \textbf{5000 W}$

If the force and motion are in different directions, you can replace F with $F\cos\theta$ to get: $\boxed{P = Fv\cos\theta}$

You **aren't** expected to **remember** this equation, but it's made up of bits that you **are supposed to know**, so be ready for the possibility of calculating **power** in a situation where the **direction of the force and direction of motion are different**.

Practice Questions

Q1 Write down the equation used to calculate work if the force and motion are in the same direction.

Q2 Write down the equation for work if the force is at an angle to the direction of motion.

Q3 Write down the equations relating i) power and work and ii) power and speed.

Exam Questions

Q1 A traditional narrowboat is drawn by a horse walking along the towpath. The horse pulls the boat at a constant speed between two locks which are 1500 m apart. The tension in the rope is 100 N at 40° to the direction of motion.

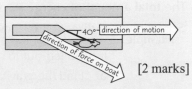

    a) How much work is done on the boat? [2 marks]

    b) The boat moves at 0.8 ms^{-1}. Calculate the power supplied to the boat. [2 marks]

Q2 A motor is used to lift a 20 kg load a height of 3 m. ($g = 9.81$ ms^{-2})

    a) Calculate the work done in lifting the load. [2 marks]

    b) The speed of the load during the lift is 0.25 ms^{-1}. Calculate the power delivered by the motor. [2 marks]

Work — there's just no getting away from it...

Loads of equations to learn. Well, that's what you came here for, after all. Can't beat a good bit of equation-learning, as I've heard you say quietly to yourself when you think no one's listening. Aha, can't fool me. Ahahahahahahahahahaha.

MODULE 3: SECTION 3 — WORK, ENERGY AND POWER

Conservation of Energy and Efficiency

Energy can never be *lost*. I repeat — *energy* can *never* be lost.

Kinetic Energy — the Energy an Object has Because it is Moving

Kinetic energy is energy an object has due to its **movement**. You can calculate it using the equation $E_k = \frac{1}{2}mv^2$, where *v* is the velocity it's travelling at and *m* is its mass. You need to know how to **derive** this equation...

- The change in kinetic energy of an object equals **work done** (*Fx*, see p.40), so $E_k = Fx$.

- You know $F = ma$ (see p.29), $a = \frac{v-u}{t}$, and $x = $ average $v \times t = \frac{(u+v)}{2}t$ (see p.16).

- Substituting these into the E_k equation gives $E_k = max = m \times \frac{(v-u)}{t} \times \frac{(u+v)}{2} \times t$.

- **Cancelling** the '*t*'s and **expanding** the brackets gives you a slightly more familiar looking $E_k = \frac{1}{2}mv^2 - \frac{1}{2}mu^2$.

- The kinetic energy of an object is the kinetic energy compared to when the object is at rest, i.e. when *u* = 0 and the object has **no kinetic energy**.

- Substituting *u* = 0 into the equation above gives you: $\boxed{E_k = \frac{1}{2}mv^2}$

An Object's Gravitational Potential Energy Depends on its Position in a Field

1) **Gravitational potential energy** (E_p) is the energy an object has due to its **position** in a gravitational field. The **greater** the **height** of the object, the **greater** its gravitational potential energy.

2) You normally want to find the change in an object's E_p, which you can work out using the equation $E_p = mgh$, where *m* is the mass of the object, *h* is the change in height and *g* is the gravitational field strength.

   - The gravitational energy gained is equal to the work done in moving the object a distance *h* upwards, so $E_p = W = F \times h$.

3) Sadly you need to know the derivation for this equation too... (at least it's a bit shorter).

   - The force that work is done against is the force of **gravity**, which is equal to *mg*. So $\boxed{E_p = mgh}$.

Learn the Principle of Conservation of Energy

The **principle of conservation of energy** says that:

> Energy **cannot be created** or **destroyed**. Energy **can be transferred** from one form to another but the total amount of energy in a closed system **will not change**.

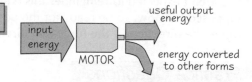

Total energy in = Total energy out

The key point to remember when answering questions is that the **total energy** will always be the same. E.g. after a **ball** is thrown **upwards**, its **kinetic energy** is converted into **gravitational potential energy**. When it **comes down** again, that **gravitational potential** energy is all **converted back** into **kinetic** energy (assuming no air resistance). The **total** amount of energy stays the **same**, but how much of it is kinetic or gravitational potential energy changes.

Example: A pendulum has a mass of 700 g and a length of 50 cm. It is pulled out to an angle of 30° from the vertical.

a) Find the gravitational potential energy stored in the pendulum bob.

Start by drawing a diagram.

You can work out the increase in height, *h*, of the end of the pendulum using trig.

$E_p = mg\Delta h = 0.7 \times 9.81 \times (0.5 - 0.5\cos30°) = 0.460... = $ **0.46 J (to 2 s.f.)**

b) The pendulum is released. Find the maximum speed of the pendulum bob as it passes the vertical position. Assume there is no air resistance.

When travelling at its maximum speed, $mgh = \frac{1}{2}mv^2$.

So $\frac{1}{2}mv^2 = 0.460...$, so $v = \sqrt{\frac{2 \times 0.460...}{0.7}} = $ **1.1 ms⁻¹ (to 2 s.f.)**

Or, you could cancel the '*m*'s and rearrange to give: $v = \sqrt{2gh}$
$= \sqrt{2 \times 9.81 \times (0.5 - 0.5\cos30°)}$
$= $ **1.1 ms⁻¹ (to 2 s.f.)**

MODULE 3: SECTION 3 — WORK, ENERGY AND POWER

Conservation of Energy and Efficiency

All Energy Transfers Involve Losses

You saw on the last page that **energy can never be created or destroyed**. But whenever **energy** is **converted** from one form to another, some is always **'lost'**. It's still there (i.e. it's **not destroyed**) — it's just not in a form you can **use**.

Most often, **energy** is lost as **heat** — e.g. **computers** and **TVs** are always **warm** when they've been on for a while. In fact, **no device** (except possibly a heater) is ever **100% efficient** (see below) because some energy is **always** lost as **heat**. (You want heaters to give out heat, but in other devices the heat loss isn't useful.) Energy can be **lost** in other forms too (e.g. **sound**) — the important thing is the lost energy **isn't** in a **useful** form and you **can't** get it back.

Often the heat that is lost is caused by **friction**. Luckily you can usually assume that **friction** is **zero** in exams.

Efficiency is the Ratio of Useful Energy Output to Total Energy Input

Efficiency is one of those words we use all the time, but it has a **specific meaning** in Physics. It's a measure of how well a **device** converts the **energy** you put **in** into the energy you **want** it to give **out**. So, a device that **wastes** loads of **energy** as heat and sound has a really **low efficiency**.

$$\text{Efficiency} = \frac{\text{useful output energy}}{\text{total input energy}} \times 100$$

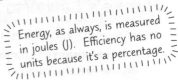
Energy, as always, is measured in joules (J). Efficiency has no units because it's a percentage.

Some questions will be kind and **give you** the **useful output energy** — others will tell you how much is **wasted**. You just have to **subtract** the **wasted energy** from the **total input energy** to find the **useful output energy**, so it's not too tricky if you keep your wits about you.

Practice Questions

Q1 State the principle of conservation of energy.

Q2 What are the equations for calculating kinetic energy and gravitational potential energy?

Q3 Show that, if there's no air resistance and the mass of the string is negligible, the speed of a pendulum is independent of the mass of the bob.

Q4 Why can a device never be 100% efficient?

Q5 What is the equation for efficiency?

Exam Questions

acceleration of free fall, g = 9.81 ms⁻²

Q1 A skateboarder is skating on a half-pipe. He lets the board run down one side of the ramp and up the other. The height of the ramp is 2.0 m.

    a) Calculate his speed at the lowest point of the ramp. Assume friction is negligible.   [3 marks]

    b) State how high he will rise up the other side of the half-pipe.   [1 mark]

    c) Real ramps are not frictionless. Describe what the skater must do to reach the top on the other side.   [1 mark]

Q2 A 20 g rubber ball is released from a height of 8 m. Assume that the effect of air resistance is negligible.

    a) Calculate the kinetic energy of the ball just before it hits the ground.   [2 marks]

    b) The ball strikes the ground and rebounds to a height of 6.5 m.
        Calculate the amount of energy that is converted to heat and sound in the impact with the ground.   [2 marks]

Q3 Calculate the efficiency of a device that wastes 65 J for every 140 J of input energy.   [1 mark]

Energy is never lost — it just sometimes prefers the scenic route...

Remember to check your answers — I can't count the number of times I've forgotten to square the velocities or to multiply by the ½... I reckon it's definitely worth the extra minute to check. You never know what you might find.

Hooke's Law

Hooke's law applies to all materials, but only up to a point. For some materials that point is so tiny you wouldn't notice...

Hooke's Law Says that Extension is Proportional to Force

If a **metal wire** is supported at the top and then a weight attached to the bottom, it **stretches**. The weight pulls down with force **F**, producing an equal and opposite force at the support.

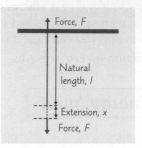

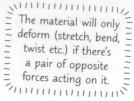

The material will only deform (stretch, bend, twist etc.) if there's a pair of opposite forces acting on it.

1) **Robert Hooke** discovered in the 17th century that the extension of a stretched wire, **x**, is proportional to the load or force, **F**. This relationship is now called **Hooke's law**.

2) Hooke's law can be written:

$$F = kx$$

Where **k** is a constant that depends on the material being stretched. **k** is called the **force constant** (or **stiffness constant**) and has units Nm^{-1}.

Hooke's Law Also Applies to Springs

A metal spring also changes length when you apply a **pair of opposite forces**.

1) The **extension** or **compression** of a spring is **proportional** to the **force** applied — so Hooke's law applies.

2) For springs, **k** in the formula **F = kx** can also be called the **spring stiffness** or **spring constant**.

> Hooke's law works just as well for **compressive** forces as **tensile** forces. For a spring, **k** has the **same value** whether the forces are tensile or compressive (that's not true for all materials).

3) **Hooke's Law** doesn't just apply to metal **springs** and **wires** — most **other materials** obey it up to a point.

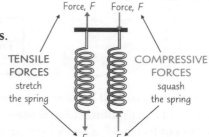

Extension and compression are sometimes called <u>tensile deformation</u> and <u>compressive deformation</u>.

Hooke's Law Stops Working when the Load is Great Enough

There's a **limit** to the force you can apply for Hooke's law to stay true.

1) The graph shows force against extension for a **typical metal wire** or **spring**.

2) The first part of the graph (up to point P) shows Hooke's law being obeyed — there's a **straight-line relationship** between **force** and **extension**.

3) When the force becomes great enough, the graph starts to **curve**. **Metals** generally obey Hooke's law up to the **limit of proportionality**, **P**.

4) The point marked **E** on the graph is called the **elastic limit**. If you exceed the elastic limit, the material will be **permanently stretched**. When all the force is removed, the material will be **longer** than at the start.

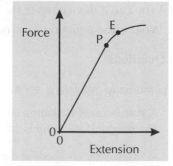

5) Be careful — there are some materials, like **rubber**, that only obey Hooke's law for **really small** extensions.

You can Combine k in Parallel or in Series

If a force is applied to more than one spring (or wire), you can **combine** the force constants of the **individual objects** to find the overall force constant of the **system**. You can then treat the system as **one spring** with force constant *k*. How you combine the force constants depends on how the springs are **arranged**:

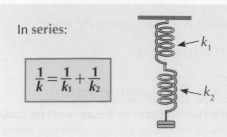

In **series**:

$$\frac{1}{k} = \frac{1}{k_1} + \frac{1}{k_2}$$

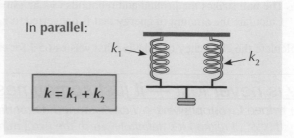

In **parallel**:

$$k = k_1 + k_2$$

Hooke's Law

A Stretch can be **Elastic** or **Plastic**

A material will show elastic deformation **up to** its **elastic limit**, and plastic deformation **beyond** it.
If a **deformation** is **elastic**, the material returns to its **original shape** once the forces are removed.

1) When the material is put under **tension**, the **atoms** of the material are **pulled apart** from one another.
2) Atoms can **move** slightly relative to their **equilibrium positions**, without changing position in the material.
3) Once the **load** is **removed**, the atoms **return** to their **equilibrium** distance apart.

If a deformation is **plastic**, the material is **permanently stretched**.

1) Some atoms in the material move position relative to one another.
2) When the load is removed, the **atoms don't return** to their original positions.

Investigating Extension

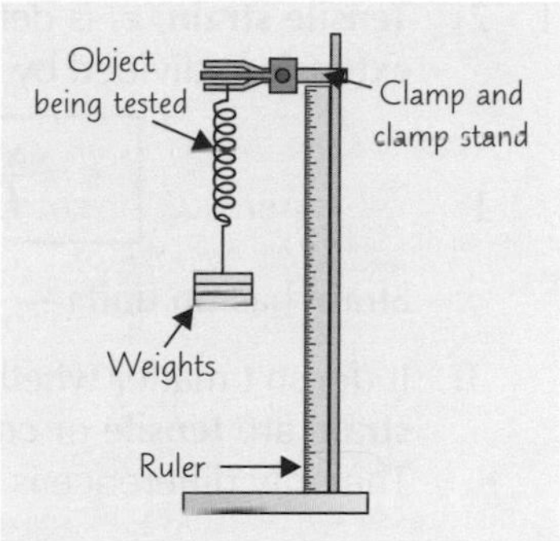

1) Set up the experiment shown in the diagram. Support the object being tested at the top (e.g. with a clamp) and measure its original length with a ruler.
2) Add weights one at a time to the bottom of the object.
3) After each weight is added, measure the new length of the object, then **calculate the extension**:

   > **extension = new length – original length**

4) Plot a graph of **force** (weight) against **extension** for your results.
   Where the line of best fit is **straight**, then the object obeys Hooke's law and the gradient = **k** (as $F = kx$). If you've loaded the object beyond its limit of proportionality, the graph will start to curve.
5) Make sure you carry out the experiment **safely**. You should be **standing up** so you can get out of the way quickly if the weights fall, and wearing **safety goggles** to protect your eyes in case the object snaps.

Object being tested — Clamp and clamp stand

Weights

Ruler

Practice Questions

Q1 State Hooke's law and explain what is meant by the elastic limit of a material.

Q2 Define tensile forces and compressive forces.

Q3 From studying the force-extension graph for a material as it is loaded and unloaded, how can you tell:
   a) if Hooke's law is being obeyed,   b) if the elastic limit has been reached?

Q4 What is meant by plastic deformation of a material?

Q5 Describe how you could investigate the effect of force on extension for a length of wire.

Exam Questions

Q1 A metal guitar string stretches 4.0 mm when a 10 N force is applied.

   a) If the string obeys Hooke's law, calculate how far the string will stretch when a 15 N force is applied.   [1 mark]

   b) Calculate the force constant for this string in Nm^{-1}.   [1 mark]

   c) The string is then stretched beyond its elastic limit. Describe the effect this will have on the string.   [1 mark]

Q2 A rubber band is 6.0 cm long. When it is loaded with 2.5 N, its length becomes 10.4 cm.
   Further loading increases the length to 16.2 cm when the force is 5.0 N.

   Does the rubber band obey Hooke's law when the force on it is 5.0 N? Explain your answer.   [2 marks]

Sod's Law — if you don't learn it, it'll be in the exam...

Three things you didn't know about Robert Hooke — he was the first person to use the word 'cell' (as in biology, not prisons), he helped Christopher Wren with his designs for St. Paul's Cathedral and no-one's sure what he looked like. I'd like to think that if I did all that stuff, then someone would at least remember what I looked like — poor old Hooke.

Stress, Strain and Elastic Potential Energy

How much a material stretches for a particular applied force depends on its dimensions.
If you want to compare one material to another, you need to use stress and strain instead.
A stress-strain graph is the same for any sample of a particular material — the size of the sample doesn't matter.

A Stress Causes a Strain

A material subjected to a pair of **opposite forces** might **deform**, i.e. **change shape**.
If the forces **stretch** the material, they're **tensile**. If the forces **squash** the material, they're **compressive**.

1) **Tensile stress**, σ, is defined as the **force applied**, F, divided by the **cross-sectional area**, A:

$$\sigma = \frac{F}{A}$$

The **units** of stress are Nm^{-2} or pascals, **Pa**.

2) **Tensile strain**, ε, is defined as the **change in length**, i.e. the **extension**, divided by the **original length** of the material:

$$\varepsilon = \frac{x}{l}$$

Strain has **no units** — it's just a **number**.

3) It doesn't matter whether the forces producing the **stress** and **strain** are **tensile** or **compressive** — the **same equations** apply.
The only difference is that you tend to think of **tensile** forces as **positive**, and **compressive** forces as **negative**.

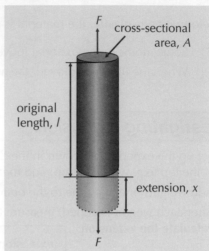

The Ultimate Tensile Strength is the Maximum Stress a Material can Take

As a greater and greater tensile **force** is applied to a material, the **stress** on it **increases**.

1) The effect of the **stress** is to start to **pull** the **atoms apart** from one another.

2) Eventually the stress becomes **so great** that atoms **separate completely**, and the **material breaks**. This is shown by point **B** on the graph. The stress at which this occurs is called the **breaking stress**.

3) The point marked **UTS** on the graph is called the **ultimate tensile strength**. This is the **maximum stress** that the material can withstand before breaking.

4) **Engineers** have to consider the **UTS** and **breaking stress** of materials when designing a **structure**.

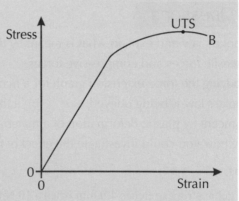

Elastic Potential Energy is the Energy Stored in a Stretched Material

When a material is **stretched** or **compressed**, **work** is done in **deforming** the material.

1) On a **graph** of **force against extension**, the **work done** is given by the **area under the graph**.

2) **Before the elastic limit, all the work done** in stretching or compressing the material is **stored** as **potential energy** in the material.

3) This stored energy is called **elastic potential energy**. There's more about how to calculate elastic potential energy on the next page.

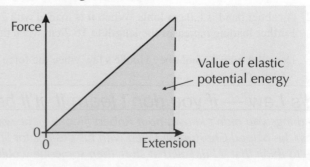

Stress, Strain and Elastic Potential Energy

You can Calculate the **Energy Stored** in a **Stretched Wire**

Provided a material obeys Hooke's law, the **potential energy** stored inside it can be **calculated** quite easily.

1) The work done on the wire in stretching it is equal to the energy stored.

2) **Work done** equals **force × displacement**.

3) However, the **force** on the material **isn't constant**. It rises from zero up to force *F*. To calculate the **work done**, use the average force between zero and *F*, i.e. ½*F*.

$$\text{work done} = \tfrac{1}{2}Fx$$

This is the triangular area under the force-extension graph — see previous page.

4) Then the **elastic potential energy**, *E*, is:

$$E = \tfrac{1}{2}Fx$$

5) Because Hooke's law is being obeyed, $F = kx$, which means *F* can be replaced in the equation to give:

$$E = \tfrac{1}{2}kx^2$$

6) If the material is stretched beyond the **elastic limit**, some work is done separating atoms. This will **not** be **stored** as elastic potential energy and so isn't released when the force is removed.

Practice Questions

Q1 Write a definition for tensile stress.

Q2 Explain what is meant by the tensile strain on a material.

Q3 What is meant by the ultimate tensile strength of a material?

Q4 How can the work done be found from the force against extension graph of a material under load?

Q5 The work done is usually calculated as force multiplied by displacement. Explain why the work done in stretching a wire is ½*Fx*.

Exam Questions

Q1 A steel wire is 2.00 m long. When a 300 N force is applied to the wire, it stretches 4.0 mm. The wire has a circular cross-section with a diameter of 1.0 mm.

    a) Calculate the tensile strain of the wire.   [1 mark]

    b) Calculate the tensile stress on the wire.   [2 marks]

Q2 A copper wire (which obeys Hooke's law) is stretched by 3.0 mm when a force of 50 N is applied.

    a) Calculate the force constant for this wire in Nm^{-1}.   [1 mark]

    b) Calculate the value of the elastic potential energy in the stretched wire.   [1 mark]

Q3 A pinball machine contains a spring which is used to fire a small, 12.0 g metal ball to start the game. The spring has a stiffness constant of 40.8 Nm^{-1}. It is compressed by 5.00 cm and then released to fire the ball.

    Calculate the maximum possible speed of the ball.   [3 marks]

UTS a laugh a minute, this stuff...

Bet you thought I was going to make a joke about this being stressful then, didn't you? There's a pile of equations to learn on these pages, as well a couple of graphs to drill into your brain, and they all might come up in the exam, so you need to learn the lot I'm afraid. Plus, it'll come in handy if you ever want to, I dunno, build a skyscraper or something.

The Young Modulus

Busy chap, Thomas Young. He did this work on tensile stress as something of a sideline. Light was his main thing. He proved that light behaved like a wave, explained how we see in colour and worked out what causes astigmatism.

The **Young Modulus** is Stress ÷ Strain

When you apply a **load** to stretch a material, it experiences a **tensile stress**, σ, and a **tensile strain**, ε.

1) Up to a point called the **limit of proportionality** (see p.44), the stress and strain of a material are proportional to each other.

2) So below this limit, for a particular material, stress divided by strain is a constant. This constant is called the **Young modulus**, **E**.

$$\text{Young modulus} = \frac{\text{tensile stress}}{\text{tensile strain}}$$

$$E = \frac{\sigma}{\varepsilon} = \frac{F \div A}{x \div l} = \frac{Fl}{xA}$$

Where **F** = force in N, **A** = cross-sectional area in m², **l** = unstretched length in m and **x** = extension in m.

3) The **units** of the Young modulus are the same as stress (**Nm⁻²** or pascals), since strain has no units.

4) The Young modulus is used by **engineers** to make sure their materials can withstand sufficient forces.

To **Find** the Young Modulus, You Need a **Very Long Wire**

This is the experiment you're most likely to do in class:

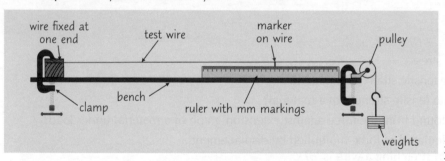

"Okay, found one. Now what?"

1) The test wire should be thin, and as long as possible. The **longer and thinner** the wire, the more it **extends** for the same force. This reduces the **uncertainty** (p.8) in your measurements.

2) First you need to find the **cross-sectional area** of the wire. Use a **micrometer** to measure the **diameter** of the wire in several places and take an **average** of your measurements. By assuming that the cross-section is **circular**, you can use the formula for the area of a circle: ⟹ | **area of a circle = πr^2**

If you're doing this experiment, make sure you're standing up so you can get out of the way quickly if the weights fall. And wear safety goggles — if the wire snaps, it could get very messy...

3) **Clamp** the wire to the bench (as shown in the diagram above) so you can hang **weights** off one end of it. Start with the **smallest weight** necessary to **straighten** the wire. (**Don't** include this weight in your final calculations.)

4) Measure the **distance** between the **fixed end of the wire** and the **marker** — this is your unstretched length.

5) Then if you increase the weight, the **wire stretches** and the **marker moves**.

6) **Increase** the **weight** in steps (e.g. 1 N intervals), recording the marker reading each time — the **extension** is the **difference** between this reading and the **unstretched length**. Use a **mass meter** or a set of **digital scales** to accurately find the weight you add at each step.

7) You can use your results from this experiment to calculate the **stress** and **strain** on the wire and plot a stress-strain graph (see next page).

To reduce random errors you should use a thin marker on the wire, and always look from directly above the marker and ruler when measuring the extension.

As you unload the wire, re-measure the extension for each weight to make sure you haven't gone past the wire's elastic limit.

(The other standard way of measuring the Young modulus in the lab is using **Searle's apparatus**. This is a bit more accurate, but it's harder to do and the equipment's more complicated.)

The Young Modulus

Plot a **Stress-Strain Graph** of Your Results to Find **E**

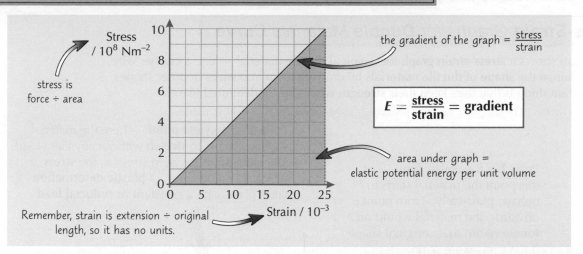

Stress / 10^8 Nm^{-2}

stress is force ÷ area

the gradient of the graph = $\frac{stress}{strain}$

$$E = \frac{\textbf{stress}}{\textbf{strain}} = \textbf{gradient}$$

area under graph = elastic potential energy per unit volume

Remember, strain is extension ÷ original length, so it has no units.

Strain / 10^{-3}

1) The **gradient** of the graph gives the Young modulus, **E**.
2) The **area under the graph** gives the **elastic potential energy** (or energy stored) **per unit volume** (i.e. the energy stored per 1 m^3 of wire).
3) The stress-strain graph is a **straight line** provided that Hooke's law is obeyed, so you can also calculate the energy per unit volume as:

Energy per unit volume = ½ $\sigma\varepsilon$

Example: The stress-strain graph above is for a thin metal wire. Find the Young modulus of the wire from the graph.

E = stress ÷ strain = gradient

The gradient of the graph = $\frac{\Delta stress}{\Delta strain} = \frac{10 \times 10^8}{25 \times 10^{-3}}$

$= \textbf{4} \times \textbf{10}^{\textbf{10}} \textbf{ Nm}^{-2}$

Practice Questions

Q1 Define the Young modulus for a material. What are the units for the Young modulus?

Q2 Describe an experiment to find the Young modulus of a test wire. Explain why a thin test wire is used.

Q3 What is given by the area contained under a stress-strain graph?

Exam Questions

Q1 A steel wire is stretched elastically. For a load of 80 N, the wire extends by 3.6 mm. The original length of the wire is 2.50 m and its average diameter is 0.6 mm.

a) Calculate the cross-sectional area of the wire in m^2. [1 mark]

b) Find the tensile stress applied to the wire. [1 mark]

c) Calculate the tensile strain of the wire. [1 mark]

d) Calculate the value of the Young modulus for steel. [2 marks]

Q2 The Young modulus for copper is 1.3×10^{11} Nm^{-2}.

a) The stress on a copper wire is 2.6×10^8 Nm^{-2}. Calculate the strain of the wire. [2 marks]

b) The load applied to the copper wire is 100 N. Calculate the average cross-sectional area of the wire. [1 mark]

c) Calculate the elastic potential energy per unit volume for this loaded wire. [1 mark]

Learn that experiment — it's important...

Getting back to the good Dr Young... As if ground-breaking work in light, the physics of vision and materials science wasn't enough, he was also a well-respected physician, a linguist and an Egyptologist. He was one of the first to try to decipher the Rosetta stone (he didn't get it right, but nobody's perfect). Makes you feel kind of inferior, doesn't it?

Interpreting Stress-Strain Graphs

Remember the stress-strain graph from page 49? Well, it turns out that because materials have different properties, their stress-strain graphs look different too — you need to know the graphs for ductile, brittle and polymeric materials.

Stress-Strain Graphs for Ductile Materials Curve

The diagram shows a **stress-strain graph** for a typical **ductile** material — e.g. a copper wire. You can change the **shape** of **ductile materials** by drawing them into **wires** or other shapes. The important thing is that they **keep their strength** when they're deformed like this.

Point **Y** is the **yield point** — here the material suddenly starts to **stretch** without any extra load. The **yield point** (or yield stress) is the **stress** at which a large amount of **plastic deformation** takes place with a **constant** or **reduced load**.

Point **E** is the **elastic limit** — at this point the material starts to behave **plastically**. From point E onwards, the material would **no longer** return to its **original shape** if the stress were removed.

Point **P** is the **limit of proportionality** — after this, the graph is no longer a straight line but starts to **bend**. At this point, the material **stops** obeying **Hooke's law**, but would still **return** to its **original shape** if the stress were removed.

Before point **P**, the graph is a **straight line** through the **origin**. This shows that the material is obeying **Hooke's law** (page 44).

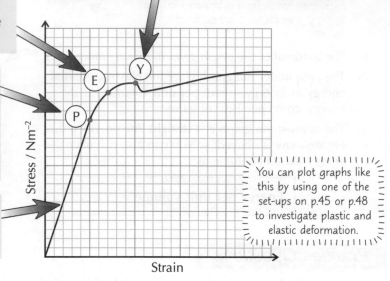

You can plot graphs like this by using one of the set-ups on p.45 or p.48 to investigate plastic and elastic deformation.

Stress-Strain Graphs for Brittle Materials Don't Curve

The graph shown below is typical of a **brittle** material.

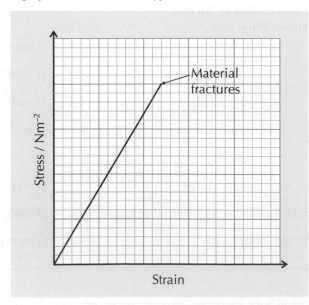

Material fractures

1) The graph starts the same as the one above — with a **straight line through the origin**. So brittle materials also obey **Hooke's law**.

2) However, when the **stress** reaches a certain point, the material **snaps** — it doesn't deform plastically.

3) When **stress** is applied to a brittle material, **tiny cracks** at the material's surface get **bigger** and **bigger** until the material **breaks** completely.

4) This is called **brittle fracture**.

Hooke's law — it's the pirates' code... yarr

Interpreting Stress-Strain Graphs

Rubber and Polythene Are Polymeric Materials

1) The **molecules** that make up **polymeric** (or polymer) **materials** are arranged in **long chains**.

2) They have a **range** of properties, so different polymers have different **stress-strain graphs**.

Example: This is the stress-strain graph for **polythene**.

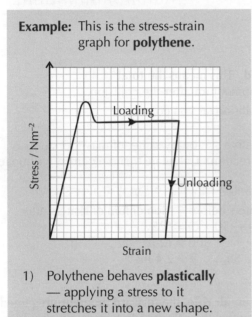

1) Polythene behaves **plastically** — applying a stress to it stretches it into a new shape.
2) Polythene is a **ductile** material.

Example: This is the stress-strain graph for **rubber**.

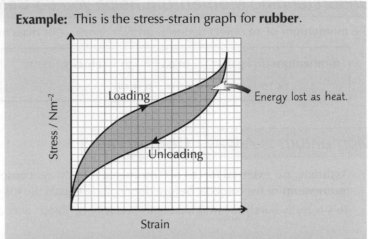

1) **Rubber** returns to its original length when the load is removed — it behaves **elastically**.

2) The loading and unloading curves for rubber are **different**. The energy released when the rubber is unloaded is **less** than the work done to stretch the rubber. This is because some of the elastic potential energy stored in the stretched rubber is **converted to heat**.

3) The amount of energy converted to heat per unit volume is given by the **area between the loading and unloading curves**.

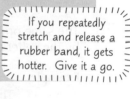
If you repeatedly stretch and release a rubber band, it gets hotter. Give it a go.

Practice Questions

Q1 Define the terms ductile and brittle. Sketch typical stress-strain graphs for ductile and brittle materials.

Q2 What is the difference between the limit of proportionality and the elastic limit?

Q3 What are polymeric materials?

Exam Questions

Q1 Hardened steel is a hard, brittle form of steel made by heating it up slowly and then quenching it in cold water.

a) Sketch a stress-strain graph for hardened steel. [1 mark]

b) Describe how the behaviour of hardened steel under increasing load will differ from that of ductile copper. [2 marks]

Q2 The graph on the left shows a stress-strain curve for mild steel.

a) State which letter, A-E, corresponds to the steel's limit of proportionality. [1 mark]

b) State which letter, A-E, corresponds to the steel's yield point. [1 mark]

My sister must be brittle — she's always snapping...

In case you were wondering, I haven't just drawn the graphs on these two pages for fun (though I did enjoy myself) — they're there for you to learn. I find the best way to remember each one is to understand why it has the shape it does — if that sounds too much like hard work, then at least make sure you can describe the shape of all four of them.

Momentum and Impulse

Linear momentum is just momentum in a straight line (not a circle or anything complicated like that).

Understanding **Momentum** helps you do **Calculations** on **Collisions**

The **momentum** of an object depends on two things — its **mass** and **velocity**:

> **momentum** (in kg ms⁻¹) = **mass** (in kg) × **velocity** (in ms⁻¹)
>
> or in symbols: $p = mv$

Momentum is a vector quantity (see p.14), so just like velocity, it has size and direction.

Momentum is Always **Conserved**

1) Assuming **no external forces** act, momentum is always **conserved**. This means the **total momentum** of two objects **before** they collide **equals** the total momentum **after** the collision.

2) This is really handy for working out the **velocity** of objects after a collision (as you do...):

Example: A skater of mass 75 kg and velocity 4 ms⁻¹ collides with a stationary skater of mass 50 kg. The skaters join together and move off in the same direction. Calculate their velocity after impact.

BEFORE   AFTER

4 ms⁻¹ 0 ms⁻¹ $v = ?$
75 kg   50 kg   125 kg

Before you start a momentum calculation, always draw a quick sketch.

Momentum of skaters before = Momentum of skaters after
$$(75 \times 4) + (50 \times 0) = 125v$$
$$300 = 125v$$
So... $v = \textbf{2.4 ms}^{-1}$

3) The same principle can be applied in **explosions**. E.g. if you fire an **air rifle**, the **forward momentum** gained by the pellet **equals** the **backward momentum** of the rifle, and you feel the rifle recoiling into your shoulder.

Example: A bullet of mass 0.005 kg is shot from a rifle at a speed of 200 ms⁻¹. The rifle has a mass of 4 kg. Calculate the velocity at which the rifle recoils.

4 kg, $v = ?$ 0.005 kg, 200 ms⁻¹

Momentum before explosion = Momentum after explosion
$$0 = (0.005 \times 200) + (4 \times v)$$
$$0 = 1 + 4v \quad \text{so} \quad v = \textbf{-0.25 ms}^{-1}$$

4) In reality, collisions and explosions usually happen in more than one dimension. In **two-dimensional collisions**, momentum is conserved in **both dimensions**. You can solve two-dimensional collision problems by **resolving vectors** (see page 15).

Example: Ball A collides with stationary ball B, as shown in diagram 1. After the collision, the two balls move off as shown in diagram 2. Ball A has a mass of 40 g. Calculate the mass, m, of ball B.

DIAGRAM 1

Ball B

36.9° 10 ms⁻¹

Ball A

NOT TO SCALE

DIAGRAM 2

36.9°
5 ms⁻¹   66.0°
Ball A   6.57 ms⁻¹
            Ball B

You can work this using conservation of momentum in just the horizontal direction (or just the vertical). Start by picking the positive direction — let's say right is positive.

horizontal momentum before the collision = horizontal momentum after the collision

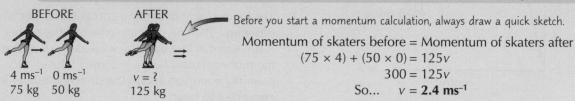
$$(0.04 \times 10 \sin 36.9°) + (m \times 0) = -(0.04 \times 5 \sin 36.9°) + (m \times 6.57 \sin 66.0°)$$

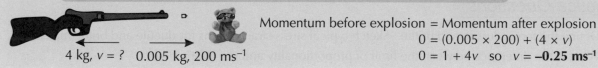
so, $m = \dfrac{0.04 \times (10 \sin 36.9° + 5 \sin 36.9°)}{6.57 \sin 66.0°} = 0.0600... \text{ kg} = \textbf{60 g (to 2 s.f.)}$

The horizontal component of the velocity of ball A is negative after the collision — it's to the left.

You could check your answer by doing the same calculation for the vertical direction.

Momentum and Impulse

Collisions can be Elastic or Inelastic

A **perfectly elastic** collision is one where **momentum** is **conserved** and **kinetic energy** is **conserved** — i.e. no energy is dissipated as heat, sound, etc. If a collision is **inelastic** it means that some of the kinetic energy is converted into other forms during the collision. But **momentum is always conserved.**

Example: A toy lorry (mass 2.0 kg) travelling at 3.0 ms^{-1} crashes into a smaller toy car (mass 800 g to 2 s.f.), travelling in the same direction at 2.0 ms^{-1}. The velocity of the lorry after the collision is 2.6 ms^{-1} in the same direction. Calculate the new velocity of the car and the total kinetic energy (KE) before and after the collision.

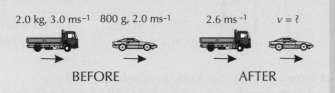

2.0 kg, 3.0 ms^{-1} 800 g, 2.0 ms^{-1} 2.6 ms^{-1} $v = ?$

BEFORE   AFTER

Momentum before collision = Momentum after collision
$(2.0 \times 3.0) + (0.80 \times 2.0) = (2.0 \times 2.6) + (0.80v)$
$7.6 = 5.2 + 0.80v$
$2.4 = 0.80v$ so $v =$ **3.0 ms^{-1}**

KE before = KE of lorry + KE of car
$= \frac{1}{2}mv^2$ (lorry) $+ \frac{1}{2}mv^2$ (car)
$= \frac{1}{2}(2.0 \times 3.0^2) + \frac{1}{2}(0.80 \times 2.0^2)$
$= 9 + 1.6 =$ **11 J (to 2 s.f.)**

KE after $= \frac{1}{2}(2.0 \times 2.6^2) + \frac{1}{2}(0.80 \times 3.0^2)$
$= 6.76 + 3.6 =$ **10 J (to 2 s.f.)**

The difference in the two values is the amount of kinetic energy <u>dissipated</u> as heat or sound, or in damaging the vehicles — so this is an <u>inelastic collision</u>.

You can use the rule of the conservation of momentum, (and the conservation of kinetic energy in elastic collisions) to predict the behaviour of real-world objects, for example balls in sports games.

Impulse = Change in Momentum

1) Newton's second law says **force = rate of change of momentum** (see page 54), or $F = \Delta p \div \Delta t$

2) **Rearranging** Newton's 2nd law gives:
   Impulse is defined as **average force × time**, $F\Delta t$.
   The units of impulse are **newton seconds**, Ns.

   $$F\Delta t = \Delta p$$
   so **impulse = change of momentum**

3) The area under a force-time graph is $F \times \Delta t =$ impulse.

   See p.25 for how to estimate the area under non-linear graphs.

Practice Questions

Q1 Give two examples of conservation of momentum in practice.

Q2 How is calculating the momentum before and after a collision different when objects collide in two dimensions rather than one?

Q3 Describe how to find the impulse of a collision from a force-time graph.

Exam Question

Q1 A snooker ball of mass 0.145 kg moving at 1.94 ms^{-1} collides with a stationary snooker ball of mass 0.148 kg. The first ball rebounds along its initial path at 0.005 ms^{-1}, and the second ball moves off in the opposite direction.

   a) Calculate the velocity of the second ball immediately after the collision. [2 marks]

   b) State whether or not the collision is perfectly elastic. Explain your answer. [3 marks]

   c) The first ball then hits the cushion at the edge of the table and comes to a stop. The collision takes 0.15 seconds. Calculate the average force experienced by the ball in this collision. [2 marks]

Momentum will never be an endangered species — it's always conserved...

Remember, impulse is only talking about the change of momentum of one of the objects, whilst conservation of momentum applies to the whole system. So the impulse of an object can change although momentum is conserved.

Newton's Laws of Motion

You did most of this at GCSE, but that doesn't mean you can just skip over it now. You'll be kicking yourself if you forget this stuff in the exam — it's easy marks...

Newton's **1st Law** says that a **Force** is Needed to Change Velocity

1) On page 28, you saw that a net force is needed for an object to **accelerate**.

2) **Newton's 1st law of motion** states that the **velocity** of an object will **not change** unless a **net force** acts on it.

3) In plain English this means a body will remain at rest or continue to move in a **straight line** at a **constant speed**, unless acted on by a **net force**.

An apple sitting on a table won't go anywhere because the **forces** on it are **balanced**.

reaction (*R*) = weight (*mg*)

(force of table pushing apple up) (force of gravity pulling apple down)

4) If the forces **aren't balanced**, the **overall net force** will cause the body to **accelerate** — if you gave the apple above a shove, there'd be a net force acting on it and it would roll off the table. Acceleration can mean a change in **direction**, or **speed**, or both. (See Newton's 2nd law, below.)

Newton's **2nd Law** says that Force is the **Rate of Change in Momentum**

Newton's 2nd Law states that:

> "The **rate of change of momentum** of an object is **directly proportional** to the **net force** which acts on the object."   or $F = \dfrac{\Delta p}{\Delta t}$

Remember, $p = mv$, (see page 52).

If mass is constant, this can be written as:

> **net force = mass × acceleration**   or $F = ma$

See page 29 for more on this equation.

Example: Sarah is playing hockey. The ball is coming towards her at a speed of 4.6 ms⁻¹. She hits it so that it travels back in the same direction at a speed of 10.2 ms⁻¹. Her stick is in contact with the ball for 0.84 seconds. The ball has a mass of 161 g. Calculate the average force exerted on the ball during this time.

Use $F = \dfrac{\Delta p}{\Delta t}$: $\Delta p = 0.161 \times 10.2 - 0.161 \times (-4.6)$
$= 0.161 \times (10.2 + 4.6)$
$= 2.3828 \text{ kg ms}^{-1}$

The ball reverses direction, so you need to give one of the velocities a negative value. Choose whichever makes the maths easier.

$\Delta t = 0.84$ s

$F = 2.3828 \div 0.84 = 2.8366... = \mathbf{2.84 \text{ N (to 3 s.f.)}}$

F = ma is a **Special Case** of Newton's **2nd Law**

Newton's 2nd law says that if the **mass** of an object is **constant**, then the **bigger** the **force** acting on it, the **greater** its **acceleration** — i.e. *F = ma*. But, if the **mass** of the object is **changing** — e.g. if it is accelerating at close to the **speed of light** — then you **can't** use *F = ma*. (You don't need to know why this happens.)

Don't worry though — **Newton's 2nd law still applies**, it's just that the 'rate of **change of momentum**' bit refers to a **change in mass** and velocity.

Daisy always knew she was special.

Newton's Laws of Motion

Newton's **3rd Law** says each Force has an **Equal**, **Opposite Reaction Force**

There are a few different ways of stating Newton's 3rd law, but the clearest way is:

> **If an object A EXERTS a FORCE on object B, then**
> **object B exerts AN EQUAL BUT OPPOSITE FORCE on object A.**

You'll also hear the law as "every action has an equal and opposite reaction". But this confuses people who wrongly think the forces are both applied to the same object. (If that were the case, you'd get a resultant force of zero and nothing would ever move anywhere...)

The two forces actually represent the **same interaction**, just seen from two **different perspectives**:

1) If you **push against a wall**, the wall will **push back** against you, **just as hard**. As soon as you stop pushing, so does the wall. Amazing...

2) If you **pull a cart**, whatever force **you exert** on the rope, the rope exerts the **exact opposite** pull on you.

3) When you go **swimming**, you push **back** against the water with your arms and legs, and the water pushes you **forwards** with an equal-sized force.

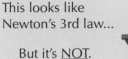
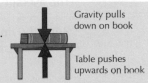

This looks like Newton's 3rd law...

But it's NOT.

Gravity pulls down on book

Table pushes upwards on book

...because both forces are acting on the book, and they're not of the same type. These are two separate interactions. The forces are equal and opposite, resulting in zero acceleration, so this is an example of Newton's 1st law.

Newton's 3rd law applies in **all situations** and to all **types of force**. But the pairs of forces are always the **same type**, e.g. both gravitational or both electrical.

Newton's 3rd law is a consequence of the **conservation of momentum** (page 52). A **net force** acting on an object means a change in **acceleration** ($F = ma$) — which means a **change in momentum**. Momentum is always **conserved**, so whenever one object exerts a force on another (and changes its momentum) the second object must exert an equal-sized force back onto the first object so that the overall change in momentum is zero.

Practice Questions

Q1 State Newton's 1st, 2nd and 3rd laws of motion, and explain what they mean.

Q2 Sketch a force diagram of a book resting on a table to illustrate Newton's 3rd law.

Exam Questions

Q1 A parachutist with a mass of 78 kg jumps out of a plane. As she falls, the net force acting on her changes.

a) Use Newton's 2nd law to explain why she initially accelerates. [2 marks]

b) Calculate the initial vertical force on the parachutist. ($g = 9.81$ ms^{-2}) [1 mark]

c) After a time, the parachutist reaches terminal velocity and stops accelerating.
Use Newton's 1st law to explain why the net force on the parachutist is zero at this point. [1 mark]

Q2 A car with mass 1244 kg increases its velocity from 5.5 ms^{-1} to 26.3 ms^{-1} over a period of 15 seconds.
The car is producing a driving force of 2143 N, and experiences frictional forces of 213 N.
The car contains two passengers. Calculate their combined mass (assume the car contains nothing else). [3 marks]

Newton's three incredibly important laws of motion...

These laws may not seem all that exciting but they're pretty powerful if you stop to think about it. These three laws are acting pretty much every time you see something moving or staying still. Which is, I'll hazard a guess, all the time. So, if you can't escape from Newton's laws, make sure you know 'em.

Car Safety

Newton's laws aren't all about apples on tables — they're also particularly important for designing cars...

If a Car **Crashes**, the Forces are Very **Large**

1) Newton's second law of motion (p.54) says:

$$F = \frac{\Delta p}{\Delta t}$$

2) When a car **crashes**, there is a big **change in speed** — possibly from 70 mph (about 110 km h⁻¹) to zero. This means there is a big change in **momentum**.

3) If the car comes to a stop **quickly** (Δt is small), then the **force acting** on the car, anyone inside it and whatever it has collided with is very **large**.

4) If Δt can be **increased**, this force can be made **much smaller** for a given change of momentum.

5) So, the **force** of an impact can be **reduced** by **increasing the time** the impact takes place over.

> **Example:** A toy car with a mass of 1 kg, travelling at 5 ms⁻¹, hits a wall and stops in a time of 0.5 seconds.
>
> The average force on the car is: $F = \frac{\Delta p}{\Delta t} = \frac{(1 \times 5) - (1 \times 0)}{0.5} = 10\,\text{N}$
>
> But if the time of impact is doubled to **1 second**, the force on the car is halved.

Most Car Safety Features are Designed to **Slow You Down Gradually**

Modern cars have lots of built-in **safety features**. A lot of them reduce the forces acting on passengers in a crash by **increasing the time** over which the **change in momentum** takes place.

Crumple Zones:

Crumple zones are areas at the front and rear of a car that are designed to **crumple on impact**. They have two effects:

1) They absorb some of the car's **kinetic energy** when they deform, which would otherwise be **transferred to the passengers** and whatever the car had collided with (e.g. other cars).

2) They **increase time** taken for the car to slow down, (Δt in the equation above) which **reduces the forces** acting on passengers and whatever the car has hit.

Air Bags:

Air bags are 'cushions' in the dashboard and elsewhere that **inflate** very quickly on collision. They protect the passengers by:

1) Making passengers **slow down more gradually** (increasing Δt).

2) Stopping passengers from hitting the dashboard, steering wheel, etc. during a crash.

Seat Belts:

Seat belts are designed to **stretch** slightly. They protect wearers in a crash by:

1) Holding the wearer **in place** in the car, stopping them from being thrown from their seats.

2) **Absorbing** some of the wearer's **kinetic energy** by stretching (p.46).

3) **Increasing the time** that the wearer comes to a stop over, Δt (again, by stretching).

> **Example:** Giles's car bumps into the back of a stationary bus. The car was travelling at 2 ms⁻¹ and comes to a stop in 0.2 s. Giles was wearing his seatbelt and takes 0.8 s to stop. Giles's mass is 75 kg.
>
> a) Calculate the average force acting on Giles during the accident.
>
> b) Calculate the average force that would have acted on Giles if he had stopped as quickly as the car.
>
> a) $F = \frac{\Delta p}{\Delta t}$ So, for Giles: $F = \frac{75 \times 2 - 75 \times 0}{0.8} = 187.5 =$ **190 N (to 2 s.f.)**
>
> b) Again, $F = \frac{\Delta p}{\Delta t}$ but $\Delta t = 0.2$ s. So: $F = \frac{75 \times 2 - 75 \times 0}{0.2} =$ **750 N (to 2 s.f.)**

Car Safety

Crash Tests are Used to Analyse the Forces in a Crash

1) Early cars didn't have many safety features in the event of a crash. But as cars became **faster** and the **number** of cars on the roads increased, car manufacturers started to think about how to make cars **safer**.

2) This led to the development of the **three-point seat belt**, **crumple zones** and **air bags** back in the 1950's.

3) At the same time, engineers were developing better ways of **understanding** the forces acting on passengers in a collision. They developed increasingly sophisticated **crash test dummies** that could **measure** all the forces that different passengers experience in different **kinds** of collisions.

4) **Crash tests** also allowed car manufacturers to test the **effectiveness** of certain **safety features**, so they could see how much they reduced the likelihood of injury.

5) Wearing a seat belt is now **mandatory** (everyone has to do it), and features such as crumple zones and air bags have become **standard features** of modern cars (along with many more sophisticated safety features).

6) Understanding the forces involved in road collisions has **saved many lives** — it's estimated that the three-point seat belt alone has saved **over a million lives worldwide** in the last 50 years.

Car Safety Features Have Some Risks

1) Seat belts can cause **bruising** during a crash.

2) They can also be dangerous for **small children** — if the top part of the belt lies across the child's **neck** this can cause injury in a crash and if the child is **too small** for a seat belt it may not **secure them properly**. In the UK, children must use **booster seats** or **cushions** to reduce these risks.

June didn't care how many safety features the car had — if Fido was driving, she wasn't getting in.

3) **Air bags** are designed for use with seat belts and can be **dangerous** if you're not wearing one. Air bags inflate very **rapidly**, with a lot of **force**. If a passenger seat belt isn't **secured properly** then the passenger can keep moving forwards quickly as the car slows down and hit the air bag as it is inflating with a **force** big enough to cause **injury**.

4) Air bags are also dangerous when using **rear-facing child seats** — the air bag inflates **behind** the child and can throw the child seat towards the car seat with some force. It is now **illegal** to use a rear-facing child seat in the UK in a seat fitted with an air bag.

Most of these risks are caused by not using a car's **safety features properly**.
If you use a seat belt and air bags as you are meant to, you are **far safer** in a car than you would be without them.

Practice Questions

Q1 Give three safety features of a car that are designed to protect passengers in the event of a crash.

Q2 Give one feature of a car's design that might protect passengers in another vehicle in the event of a collision.

Exam Question

Q1* Explain the ways that air bags protect passengers in the event of a crash, and describe some of the risks associated with their use and how these risks can be reduced. [6 marks]

*The quality of your extended response will be assessed in this question.

Here endeth the lesson...

Some real, applied physics here to get your head round, but it's important stuff. Understanding forces has had a huge effect on how cars are designed, and in doing so has saved a lot of people's lives. Not bad for a few equations, hey?

Charge, Current and Potential Difference

Electricity's brilliant, I love it. It's what gets me out of bed in the morning. (Not literally of course, that'd be quite painful.)

Current is the Rate of Flow of Charge

1) The **current** in a **wire** is like **water** flowing in a **pipe**. The **amount** of water that flows depends on the **flow rate** and the **time**. It's the same with electricity — **current is the rate of flow of charge**.

$$I = \frac{\Delta Q}{\Delta t}$$ Where I is the current in amperes, ΔQ is the charge in coulombs, and Δt is the time taken in seconds.

Remember that conventional current flows from + to –, the opposite way from electron flow.

2) The **coulomb** is the **unit of charge**.

One coulomb (C) is defined as the **amount of charge** that passes in **1 second** when the **current** is **1 ampere**.

3) You can measure the current flowing through part of a circuit using an **ammeter**. This is the circuit symbol for an ammeter:

Attach an ammeter in series with the component you're investigating.

The Charge on an Electron is the Smallest Unit of Charge

1) In electrical circuits, charge is usually carried by **electrons** (or sometimes by ions — see the next page). Electrons all carry the **same charge**, $-e$, where e is the **elementary charge**:

$$e = 1.60 \times 10^{-19}\,C$$

2) Protons carry an **opposite charge** of the **same magnitude**, $+e$.

3) The elementary charge is the **smallest unit** that charge comes in — the net charge on any particle or object will **always** be a **multiple of e**. We say that charge is **quantised**.

Potential Difference is the Work Done per Unit Charge

1) To make electric charge flow through a conductor, you need to do **work** on it.

2) **Potential difference** (p.d.), or **voltage**, is defined as the **work done per unit charge moved**:

$$W = VQ \quad or \quad V = \frac{W}{Q}$$ W is the work done in joules (see p.64). It's the energy transferred in moving the charge.

The **potential difference** across a component is **1 volt** (V) when you do **1 joule** of work moving **1 coulomb** of charge through the component. This **defines** the volt.

$$1\,V = 1\,J\,C^{-1}$$

Back to the 'water analogy' again. The p.d. is like the pressure that's forcing water along the pipe.

Resistor

6V

Here you do 6 J of work moving each coulomb of charge through the resistor, so the p.d. across it is 6 V. The energy gets converted to heat.

3) You can measure the potential difference across a component using a **voltmeter**. This is the circuit symbol for a voltmeter:

The maximum value that a voltmeter or ammeter can measure is called the full scale deflection.

4) Remember, the potential difference across components in parallel is **the same**, so the voltmeter should be connected in **parallel** with the component you're investigating.

Work Done on a Charge Equals the Kinetic Energy it Gains

1) When a **charged particle** is accelerated by a **potential difference**, the energy transferred to it is equal to the work done on the particle, $W = VQ$ (see above). For an electron (with charge of size e), this can be written as $W = Ve$.

2) The energy transferred is equal to the **kinetic energy** gained by the electron.

3) **Kinetic energy** = $\frac{1}{2}mv^2$ (see page 42), so:

$$eV = \frac{1}{2}mv^2$$ where m is the electron's mass and v is its velocity

This gives you the velocity of a single electron accelerated through a potential difference — don't get it confused with mean drift velocity (coming up on the next page).

Charge, Current and Potential Difference

The *Mean Drift Velocity* is the *Average* Velocity of the *Charge Carriers*

When **current** flows through a wire, you might imagine the **electrons** all moving uniformly in the **same direction**. In fact, they move **randomly** in **all directions**, but tend to **drift** one way. The **mean drift velocity** is just the **average velocity** and it's **much, much less** than the electrons' **actual speed**. (Their actual speed is about 10^6 ms^{-1}.)

The Current Depends on the Mean Drift Velocity:

If you're using different charge carriers, just replace e with the charge on each carrier, and let n be the number density of charge carriers.

The **current** is given by the continuity equation:

$$I = Anev$$

where: I = electrical current (A)
n = number density of electrons (m^{-3}) (number per unit volume)

v = mean drift velocity (ms^{-1})
A = cross-sectional area (m^2)
e = size of charge on one electron (C)

So...
• If you double the **number of electrons**, the **current doubles**.
• If you double the **area** the **current doubles**, like this:
• If the electrons move **twice as fast**, the **current doubles** as twice as many electrons move past a point in the same amount of time.

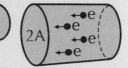

Different Materials have Different Numbers of *Charge Carriers*

1) In a **metal**, the **charge carriers** are **free electrons** — they're the ones from the **outer shell** of each atom. Thinking about the formula $I = Anev$, there are **loads** of charge carriers per unit volume, making n **big**. The **drift velocity** is **small**, even for a **high current**.

2) **Semiconductors** have **fewer charge carriers**, so the **drift velocity** needs to be **higher** to give the **same current**.

3) A **perfect insulator** wouldn't have **any charge carriers**, so $n = 0$ in the formula and you'd get **no current**. **Real** insulators have a **very small** n.

Charge Carriers in Liquids and Gases are *Ions*

1) **Ionic crystals** like sodium chloride are **insulators**. Once **molten**, though, the liquid **conducts**. Positive and negative ions are the **charge carriers**. The **same thing** happens in an **ionic solution** like copper sulfate solution.

2) A substance containing ions that conducts electricity like this is called an **electrolyte**.

3) **Gases** are **insulators**, but if you apply a **high enough voltage** electrons get **ripped out** of **atoms**, giving you **ions** along a path. You get a **spark**.

Practice Questions

Q1 Describe in words and symbols how current and charge are related.
Q2 Explain what is meant by the sentence "charge is quantised".
Q3 Define potential difference.
Q4 Write an equation for the velocity of an electron accelerated by a p.d. of V, in terms of its charge and mass.
Q5 What happens to the current in a wire if the mean drift velocity of the electrons is halved?
Q6 Describe how metals, semiconductors and insulators differ in terms of n.

Exam Questions

Q1 A battery delivers 4500 C of electric charge to a circuit in 10 minutes. Calculate the average current. [1 mark]

Q2 A kettle runs off the mains supply (230 V) and has an overall efficiency of 88%. Calculate how much electric charge will pass through the kettle if it transfers 308 J of energy to the water it contains. [2 marks]

Q3 Copper has 1.0×10^{29} free electrons per m^3. Calculate the mean drift velocity of the electrons in a copper wire of cross-sectional area 5.0×10^{-6} m^2 when it is carrying a current of 13 A. [2 marks]

I can't even be bothered to make the current joke...

Talking of currant jokes, I saw this bottle of wine the other day called 'raisin d'être' — 'raison d'être' meaning 'reason for living', but spelled slightly differently to make 'raisin', meaning 'grape'. Ho ho. Chuckled all the way home.

Resistance and Resistivity

Resistance and resistivity. Not quite the same word, not quite the same thing. Make sure you know which is which...

Everything has Resistance

1) If you put a **potential difference** (p.d.) across an **electrical component**, a **current** will flow.
2) **How much** current you get for a particular **p.d.** depends on the **resistance** of the component.
3) You can think of a component's **resistance** as a **measure** of how **difficult** it is to get a **current** to **flow** through it.

Mathematically, **resistance** is: ⟹
This equation really **defines** what is meant by resistance.

$$R = \frac{V}{I}$$

This is the **circuit symbol** for a resistor:

Learn this equation — you won't be given it in the exam.

4) **Resistance** is measured in **ohms** (Ω).

A component has a resistance of **1 Ω** if a **potential difference** of **1 V** makes a **current** of **1 A** flow through it.

Three Things Determine Resistance

If you think about a nice, **simple electrical component**, like a **length of wire**, its **resistance** depends on:

1) **Length (L)**. The **longer** the wire the **more difficult** it is to make a **current flow**.
2) **Area (A)**. The **wider** the wire the **easier** it will be for the electrons to pass along it.
3) **Resistivity (ρ)**. This **depends** on the **material** the wire's made from, as the **structure** of the material may make it easy or difficult for charge to flow. In general, resistivity depends on **environmental factors** as well, like **temperature**.

ρ is the Greek letter rho, the symbol for resistivity.

The **resistivity** of a material is defined as the **resistance** of a **1 m length** with a **1 m² cross-sectional area**, so $\rho = \frac{RA}{L}$. Resistivity is measured in **ohm metres** (Ωm).

In your exams, you'll be given this equation in the **form**:

$$R = \frac{\rho L}{A}$$

where A = cross-sectional area in m², and L = length in m

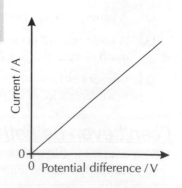

Typical values for the **resistivity** of **conductors** are **really small**.
For example, the resistivity of **copper** (at 25 °C) is just 1.72×10^{-8} Ωm.

Rho, rho, rho your boat...

However, if you **calculate** a **resistance** for a **conductor** and end up with something **really small** (e.g. 1×10^{-7} Ω), go back and **check** that you've **converted** your **area** into **m²**.

For an Ohmic Conductor, R is a Constant

A chap called **Ohm** did most of the early work on resistance. He developed a rule to **predict** how the **current** would **change** as the applied **potential difference** increased, for **certain types** of conductor.

The rule is now called **Ohm's law** and the conductors that **obey** it (mostly metals) are called **ohmic conductors**.

Provided the **temperature** is **constant**, the **current** through an ohmic conductor is **directly proportional** to the **potential difference** across it (that's **V = IR**).

1) As you can see from the graph, **doubling** the p.d. **doubles** the **current**.
2) What this means is that the **resistance** is **constant**.
3) Often **external factors**, such as **temperature** will have a **significant effect** on resistance, so you need to remember that Ohm's law is **only** true for **ohmic conductors** at **constant temperature**.

Current / A

0

0   Potential difference / V

Resistance and Resistivity

To Find the **Resistivity** of a **Wire** You Need to Find its **Resistance**

Before you start, you need to know the **cross-sectional area** of your test wire.
Assume that the wire is **cylindrical**, and so the cross-section is **circular**.

Then you can find its **cross-sectional area** using: **area of a circle = πr^2**

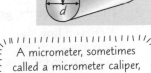

Use a **micrometer** to measure the **diameter** of the test wire in at least **three**
different points along the wire. Take an **average** value of the diameter and
divide by **2** to get the **radius** (make sure this is in m). Plug it into the equation for
cross-sectional area and... **ta da**. Now you can get your teeth into the electricity bit...

A micrometer, sometimes called a micrometer caliper, is used to precisely measure very small distances.

1) The **test wire** should be **clamped** to a ruler and connected to the rest of the circuit at the point where the ruler reads zero.

2) Attach the **flying lead** to the test wire — the lead is just a wire with a crocodile clip at the end to allow connection to any point along the test wire.

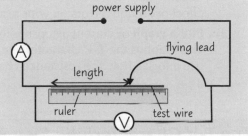

3) Record the **length** of the test wire **connected** in the circuit, the **voltmeter reading** and the **ammeter reading**.

4) Use your readings to calculate the **resistance** of the length of wire, using: $R = \dfrac{V}{I}$

5) Repeat for several **different** lengths within a sensible range, e.g. at 0.10 m intervals from 0.10 m to 1.00 m.

6) Plot your results on a graph of **resistance** against **length**, and draw a **line of best fit** (see page 6).

You could also use a digital multimeter, which can measure voltage, current and resistance.

The **gradient** of the line of best fit is equal to $\dfrac{R}{L} = \dfrac{\rho}{A}$. So **multiply** the **gradient** of the line of best fit by the **cross-sectional area** of the wire to find the resistivity of the wire material.

7) The **resistivity** of a material depends on its **temperature**, so you can only find the resistivity of a material **at a certain temperature**. Current flowing in the test wire can cause its temperature to increase, so failing to keep the wire at a **constant temperature** could invalidate your results (see p.4). Try to keep the temperature of the test wire constant by e.g. only having small currents flow through the wire.

Practice Questions

Q1 Draw the circuit symbol for a resistor.
Q2 What are the three factors that determine the resistance of a length of wire?
Q3 What is special about an ohmic conductor?
Q4 Describe an experiment to find the resistivity of a metal.

Exam Questions

Q1 Aluminium has a resistivity of 2.8×10^{-8} Ω m at 20 °C.
Calculate the resistance of a pure aluminium wire of length 4 m and diameter 1 mm, at 20 °C. [3 marks]

Q2 The table on the right shows some measurements taken by a student during an experiment investigating an unknown electrical component.

| Potential Difference (V) | 3.00 | 7.00 | 11.00 |
| Current (mA) | 4.00 | 9.33 | 14.67 |

a) Calculate the resistance of the component when a p.d. of 7.00 V is applied. [1 mark]

b) State whether the component is an ohmic conductor. Explain your answer. [3 marks]

I find the resistivity to my chat-up lines is very high...

Examiners love to ask questions about this experiment, so make sure you learn it well. Make sure you can think of some ways to reduce random errors too — e.g. by repeating measurements and by using more sensitive equipment.

I-V Characteristics

Woohoo — real physics. This stuff's actually kind of interesting.

I-V Graphs Show How Resistance Varies

Make sure you learn all the circuit symbols that come up in this section, and know how to design and use circuits using them.

1) The term '**I-V characteristic**' refers to a **graph** which shows how the **current** (I) flowing through a **component changes** as the **potential difference** (V) across it is increased.

2) The **shallower** the **gradient** of a characteristic **I-V** graph, the **greater** the **resistance** of the component.

3) A **curved line** shows that the resistance of the component **changes** with the potential difference across it.

You can investigate the *I-V* characteristic of a component using a **test circuit** like this one:

1) Use the **variable resistor** to alter the **potential difference** across the component and the **current** flowing through it, and record *V* and *I*.

2) **Repeat** your measurements and take **averages** to reduce the effect of random errors on your results.

3) **Plot a graph** of current against potential difference from your results. This graph is the **I-V characteristic** of the component and you can use it to see how the **resistance** changes.

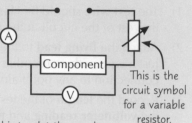
This is the circuit symbol for a variable resistor.

If you have access to a computer, you could enter your data into a spreadsheet and use this to plot the graph.

The I-V Characteristic for a Metallic Conductor is a Straight Line

1) At **constant temperature**, the **current** through a **metallic conductor**, e.g. a **wire** or a **resistor**, is **directly proportional** to the **potential difference**.

2) The fact that the characteristic graph is a **straight line through the origin** tells you that the **resistance doesn't change** — it's equal to 1 / gradient.

3) **Metallic conductors** are **ohmic** — they have **constant resistance provided** their temperature doesn't change (see below).

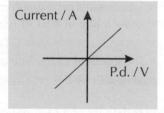

The I-V Characteristic for a Filament Lamp is Curved

Filament lamp circuit symbol:

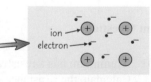

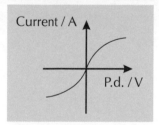

1) The characteristic graph for a **filament lamp** is a **curve**, which starts **steep** but gets **shallower** as the **potential difference rises**.

2) The **filament** in a lamp is just a **coiled up** length of **metal wire**, so you might think it should have the **same characteristic graph** as a **metallic conductor**.

3) However, **current** flowing through the lamp **increases** its **temperature**, so its **resistance increases** (see below).

The Resistivity of a Metal Increases with Temperature

1) **Charge** is carried through **metals** by **free electrons** in a **lattice** of **positive ions**.

2) Heating up a metal makes it **harder** for electrons to **move about**. The **ions vibrate more** when heated, so the electrons **collide** with them more often, **losing energy** to other forms.

ion
electron

The **resistivity** of a **metal increases** as the **temperature increases**.

This means the resistance of a metal wire increases with temperature.

Semiconductors are Used in Sensors

Semiconductors have a **higher resistivity** than **metals** because there are fewer **charge carriers** available. However, if **energy** is supplied to some types of semiconductor (e.g. by increasing temperature), **more charge carriers** are **released**, so their resistivity **decreases**. This means that they make **excellent sensors** for detecting **changes** in their environment. You need to know about **three** semiconductor components — **thermistors**, **LDRs** and **diodes**.

I-V Characteristics

The *Resistance* of a *Thermistor* Depends on *Temperature*

A **thermistor** is a **resistor** with a **resistance** that depends on its **temperature**. You only need to know about **NTC** thermistors — NTC stands for 'Negative Temperature Coefficient'. This means that the **resistance decreases** as the **temperature goes up**. The characteristic *I-V* graph for an NTC thermistor curves upwards.

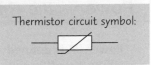
Thermistor circuit symbol:

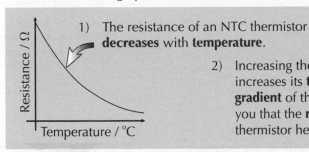

1)   The resistance of an NTC thermistor **decreases** with **temperature**.

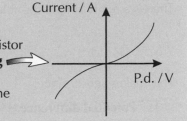
Current / A
P.d. / V

2)   Increasing the **current** through the thermistor increases its **temperature**. The **increasing gradient** of this characteristic graph tells you that the **resistance is decreasing** as the thermistor heats up.

Warming the thermistor gives more **electrons** enough **energy** to **escape** from their atoms. This means that there are **more charge carriers** available, so the resistance is lower.

The *Resistance* of an *LDR* Depends on *Light Intensity*

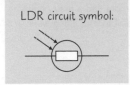
LDR circuit symbol:

LDR stands for **Light-Dependent Resistor**. The **greater** the intensity of **light** shining on an LDR, the **lower** its **resistance**.

The explanation for this is similar to that for the thermistor. In this case, **light** provides the **energy** that releases more electrons. More charge carriers means a lower resistance.

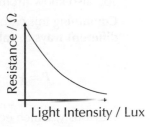
Resistance / Ω
Light Intensity / Lux

Diodes Only Let *Current Flow* in *One Direction*

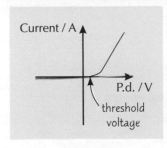
Current / A
P.d. / V
threshold voltage

Diodes (including light emitting diodes (LEDs)) are designed to let **current flow** in **one direction** only. You don't need to be able to explain how they work, just what they do.

1)   **Forward bias** is the **direction** in which the **current is allowed to flow**.

2)   **Most** diodes require a **threshold voltage** of about **0.6 V** in the **forward direction** before they will conduct.

3)   In **reverse bias**, the **resistance** of the diode is **very high** and the current that flows is **very tiny**.

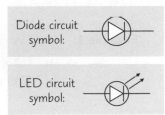
Diode circuit symbol:

LED circuit symbol:

Practice Questions

Q1 If an *I-V* graph is curved, what does this tell you about the resistance?

Q2 Sketch the test circuit used to investigate the *I-V* characteristic of a component, and explain how it is used.

Q3 Draw an *I-V* characteristic graph for a resistor.

Q4 What is an LDR?

Q5 Draw an *I-V* characteristic graph for a diode. Label the areas of forward bias and reverse bias.

Exam Question

Q1 a) Sketch a characteristic *I-V* graph for a filament lamp.   [1 mark]

b) Compare your sketch to the *I-V* graph of a thermistor. Explain any differences.   [4 marks]

You light up my world like an LED — with One-Directional current...

Make sure you learn all these graphs and can explain them all. It's all about energy — for metals, more energy means more heat and a higher resistance. For semiconductors, more energy means more charge carriers and lower resistance.

Electrical Energy and Power

Power and energy are pretty familiar concepts — and here they are again. Same principles, just different equations.

Power is the Rate of Transfer of Energy

Power (*P*) is **defined** as the **rate** of **doing work**. It's measured in **watts (W)**, where **1 watt** is equivalent to **1 joule of work done per second**.

in symbols:
$$P = \frac{W}{t}$$

There's a really simple formula for **power** in **electrical circuits**:

$$P = VI$$

⎥⎥⎥⎥⎥⎥⎥⎥⎥⎥⎥⎥⎥⎥⎥⎥⎥⎥⎥⎥⎥⎥⎥⎥⎥⎥
In an electrical circuit, *W* is the work done moving a charge.
⎥⎥⎥⎥⎥⎥⎥⎥⎥⎥⎥⎥⎥⎥⎥⎥⎥⎥⎥⎥⎥⎥⎥

This makes sense, since:

1) **Potential difference** (*V*) is defined as the **work done** per **coulomb**.
2) **Current** (*I*) is defined as the **number** of **coulombs** transferred per **second**.
3) So **p.d.** × **current** is **work done per second**, i.e. **power**.

Arnold had a pretty high resistance to doing work.

You also know (from the definition of **resistance**) that *V = IR* (see p.60).
Combining this with the equation above gives you loads of **different ways** to **calculate power**.

$$P = VI \qquad P = \frac{V^2}{R} \qquad P = I^2R$$

Obviously, which equation you should use depends on what **quantities** you're given in the **question**.

Phew... that's quite a few equations to get acquainted with.
And as if they're not exciting enough, here are some examples to get your teeth into...

Example 1: A 24 W car head lamp is connected to a 12 V car battery.
a) How much electrical energy will the lamp convert into light and heat energy in 2 hours?
b) Find the total resistance of the lamp.

a) Number of seconds in 2 hours = 2 × 60 × 60 = 7200 s
$P = W \div t$, so $W = P \times t = 24 \times 7200 = 172\ 800\ J = $ **170 kJ (to 2 s.f.)**

b) $P = \frac{V^2}{R}$ so $R = \frac{V^2}{P} = \frac{12^2}{24} = \frac{144}{24} = $ **6.0 Ω**

Example 2: A robotic mutant Santa from the future converts 750 J of electrical energy into heat every second.
a) What is the operating power of the robotic mutant Santa?
b) All of the robotic mutant Santa's components are connected in series, with a total resistance of 30 Ω. What current flows through his wire veins?

a) Power = $W \div t = 750 \div 1 = $ **750 W**

b) $P = I^2R$ so $I = \sqrt{\frac{P}{R}} = \sqrt{\frac{750}{30}} = \sqrt{25} = $ **5.0 A**

Electrical Energy and Power

Energy is Easy to Calculate if you Know the Power

Sometimes it's the **total energy** transferred that you're interested in. In this case you simply
need to **multiply** the **power** by the **time**. So:

$$W = VIt$$ (or $W = \dfrac{V^2}{R}t$ or $W = I^2Rt$)

Make sure that the time is in seconds before you use this equation.

Example: The circuit diagram on the right is part of an electric kettle.
A current of 4 A flows through the kettle's heating element
once it is connected to the mains (230 V).

The kettle takes 4.5 minutes to boil the water it contains.
How much energy does the kettle's heating element
transfer to the water in the time it takes to boil?

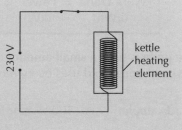

Time the kettle takes to boil in seconds = 4.5 × 60 = 270 seconds.

Use the equation $W = VIt = 230 \times 4 \times 270 = 248\,400\ \text{J} = \mathbf{250\ kJ}$ **(to 2 s.f.)**

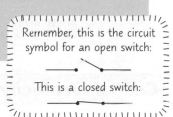

Remember, this is the circuit
symbol for an open switch:

This is a closed switch:

Practice Questions

Q1 Power is measured in watts. What is 1 watt equivalent to?

Q2 What equation links power, voltage and resistance?

Q3 Write down the equation linking power, current and resistance.

Exam Questions

Q1 The circuit diagram for a mains-powered hairdryer is shown below.

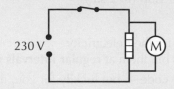

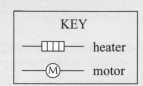

KEY	
—⊏□□⊐—	heater
—(M)—	motor

a) The heater has a power of 920 W in normal operation. Calculate the current in the heater. [1 mark]

b) The motor's resistance is 190 Ω. Calculate the current through the motor when the hairdryer is used. [1 mark]

c) Show that the total power of the hairdryer in normal operation is just under 1.2 kW. [2 marks]

Q2 A 12 V car battery supplies a current of 48 A for 2.0 seconds to the car's starter motor.
The total resistance of the connecting wires is 0.01 Ω.

a) Calculate the energy transferred by the battery in this time. [1 mark]

b) Calculate the energy wasted as heat in the wires. [1 mark]

Ultimate cosmic powers...

*Another load of equations on these pages to add to your collection, oh joy. I used to find it helped to stick big lists of
equations all over my walls in the run up to exams — the least cool wallpaper imaginable. Make sure you learn the
circuit symbol for a heater in exam question 1 — you won't get a key in the exam (I gave you one because I'm nice).*

Domestic Energy and Energy Saving

If you went into an electricity shop and asked for a 100 joule packet of electricity you'd be laughed out of town. Why? Because electricity companies use kilowatt-hours, not joules — phew, you kids don't know anything these days.

Electricity Companies Don't Use Joules and Watts

Electricity companies charge their customers for '**units**' of electricity. Another name for a unit is a **kilowatt-hour (kWh)**. If you know the **power** of an **appliance** and the **length of time** it's used for you can calculate the **work** it does in kWh.

> Remember, power is the work done per second: $P = W/t$ (see page 64).

Work Done	=	Power	×	Time
(kWh)		(kW)		(h)

1 kWh = 3.6 million joules

1 kW = 1000 W
1 hour = 3600 seconds

The **joule** is such a **small amount** of energy compared with the amount a typical household uses every month that it's **impractical**.

Example: A 1500 W hairdryer is on for 10 minutes. How much energy does it use in J and kWh?

$W = Pt = 1500 \times 10 \times 60 =$ **900 000 J (to 2 s.f.)** $W = Pt = 1.5 \times 10/60 =$ **0.25 kWh (to 2 s.f.)**

Cost of Electricity is the Price per Unit Times the Number of Units Used

To work out the **cost of electricity** you need to know **how much you've used** (in **units**) and the **price of each unit**. Then it's a simple matter of **multiplying** these two numbers together:

> **Cost = No. of units × Price per unit**

Example: How much does it cost to use an 800 W microwave oven for 6 minutes? Electricity costs 16.1p per unit.

$W = Pt = 0.8 \times 6/60 = 0.08$ kWh

Cost = units × price per unit = 0.08 × 16.1
　　　　　　　　　　　　　= 1.288 = **1.3p (to 2 s.f.)**

> Watch out for the units — you need power in kW (not watts), time in hours (not minutes or seconds) and money in either pence or pounds.

Of course, most people don't make a separate payment for their electricity each time they use a microwave — electricity providers bill them at **regular intervals** instead.

Electricity bills can look like they're written in a strange code — but luckily for you, the examples you'll see are easy to understand. Real ones aren't really that bad either — you just need to know **where to look** to find the **important information**. Take a look at the lovely **example** below:

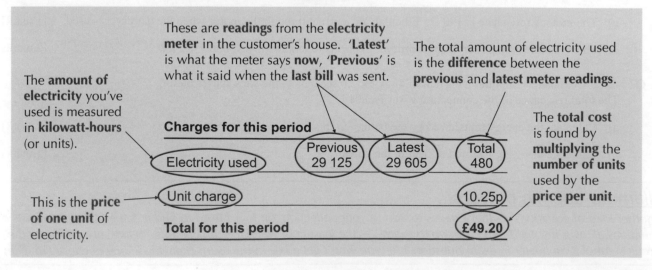

The **amount of electricity** you've used is measured in **kilowatt-hours** (or units).

These are **readings** from the **electricity meter** in the customer's house. '**Latest**' is what the meter says **now**, '**Previous**' is what it said when the **last bill** was sent.

The total amount of electricity used is the **difference** between the **previous** and **latest meter readings**.

The **total cost** is found by **multiplying** the **number of units** used by the **price per unit**.

This is the **price of one unit** of electricity.

Charges for this period

	Previous	Latest	Total
Electricity used	29 125	29 605	480
Unit charge			10.25p
Total for this period			£49.20

Domestic Energy and Energy Saving

It's *Important* to *Save Energy*

Electricity doesn't just cost a packet — producing it has **environmental impacts** too:

- Burning **fossil fuels** (**coal**, **oil** and **gas**) releases **carbon dioxide** into the atmosphere, which adds to the **greenhouse effect** and contributes to **global warming**. Sulfur dioxide released by burning oil and coal can also cause **acid rain**.
- **Nuclear** power stations produce **radioactive waste**, which can be **dangerous** to the environment and human health if it isn't **disposed of safely**.
- Even **renewable** energy sources like **biofuels** have an impact because lots of **land** is needed to produce them.

Using **energy saving devices** can not only save you **money**, but helps to **reduce these impacts**.

1) **Energy saving** (fluorescent) **light bulbs** are more expensive than **traditional filament bulbs**, but are about four times more **efficient**. They also last for about **ten years** (as opposed to a year for filament bulbs) so reduce the number of bulbs needing to be **disposed of** and **replaced**.

2) **LED light bulbs** are even **more efficient** than energy saving bulbs, and last even longer, but they **cost more**.

3) **Domestic appliances** (e.g. washing machines and ovens) sold in the UK all have an **energy rating**. This helps customers choose the appliance that's **most efficient to run**, which can reduce their **environmental impact**.

Remember, efficiency is given by:

$$\text{efficiency} = \frac{\text{useful output energy}}{\text{total input energy}} \times 100$$

Practice Questions

Q1 Why aren't joules used on electricity bills? What is used instead?

Q2 What equation would you use to find the cost of using an electrical appliance for a given amount of time?

Q3 Why is it important to think about energy efficiency when you buy domestic appliances?

Q4 Compare filament, energy saving and LED bulbs in terms of their environmental impact.

Exam Questions

Q1 A vacuum cleaner has a power of 1550 W.

   a) Calculate the energy transferred when the vacuum cleaner is operated for 15 minutes. Give your answer in:

     i) joules, [1 mark]

     ii) kilowatt-hours. [1 mark]

   b) Calculate the cost of using the vacuum cleaner for 15 minutes. Electricity costs 15.9 pence per unit. [1 mark]

Q2 A television is connected to a 230 V power supply. Electricity costs 16.2 pence per unit. When the television is in standby mode, it draws a current of 6.5 mA. Calculate the cost of leaving the television on standby for 10 hours. [3 marks]

Q3 A customer is buying a washing machine. Model A has an average power of 470 W on a typical cycle, and model B has an average power of 410 W. Model A takes 135 minutes to wash a load of laundry, and model B takes 125 minutes.

   a) Calculate how many kilowatt-hours each model uses in a typical cycle. [2 marks]

   b) The customer does two loads of laundry a week on a typical cycle. Electricity costs 16.2p per unit. Calculate how much each model of washing machine would cost him a year to run. [4 marks]

It's suddenly all got very serious, hasn't it...

Paying bills and being a responsible consumer? Bring back the circuit diagrams, I say. It's important that you learn this stuff though, as it'll not only save you money and make you a better person, but crucially it might also help you pass your exams. So turn on your energy saving lamp and give these pages another read.

E.m.f. and Internal Resistance

There's resistance everywhere — inside batteries, in all the wires (although it's very small) and in the circuit components themselves. Who said current had it easy?

Batteries have an Internal Resistance

Because the resistance of wires is so small, on these two pages I'm assuming they have zero resistance.

Resistance comes from **electrons colliding** with **atoms** and **losing energy**.

In a **battery**, **chemical energy** is used to make **electrons move**. As they move, they collide with atoms inside the battery — so batteries **must** have resistance. This is called **internal resistance**.

Internal resistance is what makes **batteries** and **cells warm up** when they're used.

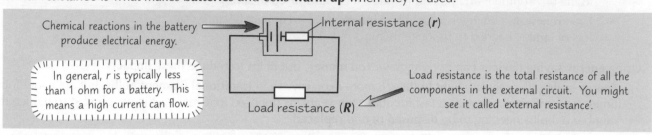

Chemical reactions in the battery produce electrical energy.

Internal resistance (**r**)

In general, *r* is typically less than 1 ohm for a battery. This means a high current can flow.

Load resistance is the total resistance of all the components in the external circuit. You might see it called 'external resistance'.

Load resistance (**R**)

1) The total amount of **work** the battery does on each **coulomb** of charge is called its **electromotive force** or **e.m.f.** (ε). Be careful — e.m.f. **isn't** actually a force. It's measured in **volts**.

$$W = \varepsilon Q \quad \text{or} \quad \varepsilon = \frac{W}{Q}$$

W is the work done on the charge (i.e. the energy transferred to the charge) in joules.

2) The **potential difference** across the **load resistance** (*R*) is the **work done** when **one coulomb** of charge flows through the **load resistance**. This potential difference is called the **terminal p.d.** (*V*).

3) If there was **no internal resistance**, the **terminal p.d.** would be the **same** as the **e.m.f.** However, in **real** power supplies, there's **always some energy lost** overcoming the internal resistance.

4) The **energy wasted per coulomb** overcoming the internal resistance is called the **lost volts** (*v*).

Conservation of energy tells us:

| energy per coulomb supplied by the source | = | energy per coulomb used in load resistance | + | energy per coulomb wasted in internal resistance |

There are Loads of Calculations with E.m.f. and Internal Resistance

Examiners can ask you to do **calculations** with **e.m.f.** and **internal resistance** in loads of **different** ways. You've got to be ready for whatever they throw at you.

$$\varepsilon = V + v \qquad \varepsilon = I(R + r)$$
$$V = \varepsilon - v \qquad \varepsilon = V + Ir$$

Learn all of these equations for the exam. Only these two will be on your formula sheet.

These are all basically the **same equation**, just written differently. If you're given enough information you can calculate the e.m.f. (ε), terminal p.d. (*V*), lost volts (*v*), current (*I*), load resistance (*R*) or internal resistance (*r*). Which equation you should use depends on what information you've got, and what you need to calculate.

You Can Work Out the E.m.f. of Multiple Cells in Series or Parallel

For cells **in series**, you can calculate the **total e.m.f.** of the cells by **adding** their individual e.m.f.s.

$$\varepsilon_{total} = \varepsilon_1 + \varepsilon_2 + \varepsilon_3 + ...$$

This makes sense if you think about it, because each charge goes through each of the cells and so gains e.m.f. from each one.

For identical cells **in parallel**, the **total e.m.f.** of the combination of cells is the **same size** as the e.m.f. of each of the individual cells.

See p.70 for all the rules for parallel and series circuits.

$$\varepsilon_{total} = \varepsilon_1 = \varepsilon_2 = \varepsilon_3 = ...$$

This is because the current will split equally between identical cells. The charge only gains e.m.f. from the cells it travels through — so the overall e.m.f. in the circuit doesn't increase.

E.m.f. and Internal Resistance

Time for an Example E.m.f. Calculation Question...

Example Three identical cells each with an e.m.f. of 2.0 V and an internal resistance of 0.20 Ω are connected in parallel in the circuit shown to the right. A current of 0.90 A is flowing through the circuit. Calculate the total p.d. across the cells.

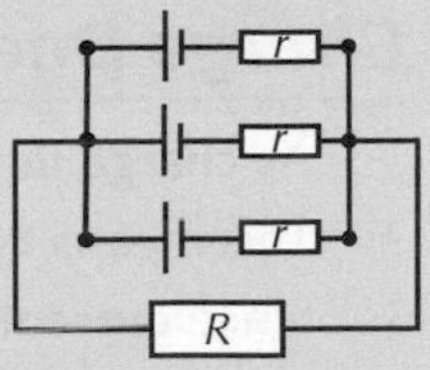

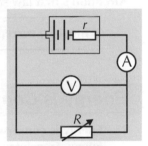

First calculate the lost volts, v, for 1 cell using $v = Ir$.

Since the current flowing through the circuit is split equally between each of the three cells, the current through one cell is $I/3$. So for 1 cell: $v = I/3 \times r = 0.90/3 \times 0.20 = 0.30 \times 0.20 = 0.06$ V

Then find the terminal p.d. across 1 cell using the equation: $V = \varepsilon - v = 2 - 0.06 = 1.94$

So the total p.d. across the cells combined = 1.94 = **1.9 V (to 2 s.f.)**

Investigate Internal Resistance and E.m.f. With This Circuit

1) **Vary** the **current** in the circuit by changing the value of the **load resistance** (R) using the variable resistor. **Measure** the **p.d.** (V) for several different values of **current** (I).

2) Record your data for V and I in a table, and **plot the results** in a graph of V against I.

To find the **e.m.f.** and **internal resistance** of the cell, start with the equation: $\boxed{\varepsilon = V + Ir}$

1) Rearrange to give $V = -rI + \varepsilon$

2) Since ε and r are constants, that's just the equation of a **straight line**:

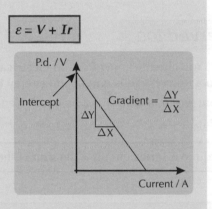

P.d. / V

Intercept

Gradient = $\frac{\Delta Y}{\Delta X}$

ΔY

ΔX

Current / A

> Equation of a straight line
> $y = mx + c$
> gradient   y-intercept

3) So the intercept on the vertical axis is ε.

4) And the gradient is $-r$.

Geoff didn't quite calculate the gradient correctly.

An **easier** way to **measure** the **e.m.f.** of a **power source** to just connect a **voltmeter** across its **terminals**. Voltmeters have a very **high resistance**, but a **small current** will still flow through them, so there must be some **lost volts**, which means you measure a value **very slightly less** than the **e.m.f.** (Although in practice the difference isn't usually significant.)

Practice Questions

Q1 What causes internal resistance? Write down the equation linking work, e.m.f. and charge.

Q2 What is the difference between e.m.f. and terminal p.d.?

Q3 What is meant by 'lost volts'?

Q4 Give an example of a source of e.m.f and describe an experiment to find the value of its e.m.f.

Exam Questions

Q1 A battery with an internal resistance of 0.8 Ω and an e.m.f. of 24 V powers a dentist's drill with resistance 4.0 Ω.

    a) Calculate the current in the circuit when the drill is connected to the power supply. [1 mark]

    b) Calculate the voltage across the drill while it is being used. [1 mark]

Q2 A bulb of resistance R is powered by two cells connected in series, each with internal resistance r and e.m.f. ε. Which expression represents the current flowing through each cell? [1 mark]

    A $\dfrac{\varepsilon}{R+r}$ **B** $\dfrac{\varepsilon}{2(R+2r)}$ **C** $\dfrac{2\varepsilon}{R+2r}$ **D** $\dfrac{\varepsilon}{R+2r}$

Why'd the physicist swallow a multimeter? To find his internal resistance...

Thank you, thank you, I'm here all week. A jam-packed pair of pages here, but it's all stuff you need to know. Make sure you know the difference between terminal p.d. and e.m.f., and that you've got a handle on all those equations.

Conservation of Charge & Energy in Circuits

There are some things in Physics that are so fundamental that you just have to accept them. Like the fact that there's loads of Maths in it. And that energy is conserved. And that Physicists get more homework than everyone else.

Charge Doesn't 'Leak Away' Anywhere — it's Conserved

1) As **charge flows** through a circuit, it **doesn't** get **used up** or **lost**.

2) This means that whatever charge flows **into** a junction will flow **out** again.

3) Since **current** is **rate of flow of charge**, it follows that whatever current flows **into** a junction is the same as the current flowing **out** of it.

> **Example:** 6 coulombs of charge flow into a junction in 1 second, and split in the ratio 1:2.
>
> $Q_1 = 6\,C \Rightarrow I_1 = 6\,A$
>
> at junction, current branches in two
>
> $Q_2 = 2\,C \Rightarrow I_2 = 2\,A$
> $Q_3 = 4\,C \Rightarrow I_3 = 4\,A$
>
> $I_1 = I_2 + I_3$

Kirchhoff's first law says:

> The total **current entering a junction** = the total **current leaving it**.

THE £1 STORE

Betsy believed in conservation of charge.

Energy is Conserved too

1) **Energy is conserved.** You already know that. In **electrical circuits**, **energy** is **transferred round** the circuit. Energy **transferred to** a unit charge is **e.m.f.**, and energy **transferred from** a unit charge is **potential difference**.

2) In a **closed loop**, these two quantities must be **equal** if energy is conserved (which it is).

Kirchhoff's second law says:

> The **total e.m.f.** around a **series circuit** = the **sum** of the **p.d.**s across each component. (or $\varepsilon = \Sigma IR$ in symbols)

You Can Apply Kirchhoff's Laws to Different Combinations of Resistors

A **typical exam question** will give you a **circuit** with bits of information missing, leaving you to fill in the gaps. Not the most fun... but on the plus side you get to ignore any internal resistance stuff (unless the question tells you otherwise)... hurrah. You need to remember the **following rules**:

Series Circuits:

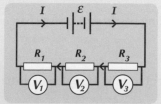

1) **same current** at **all points** of the circuit (since there are no junctions)

2) **e.m.f. split** between **components** (by Kirchhoff's 2nd law), so:
$\varepsilon = V_1 + V_2 + V_3$

3) $V = IR$, so if I is constant:
$IR_{total} = IR_1 + IR_2 + IR_3$

4) cancelling the Is gives:

> $R_{total} = R_1 + R_2 + R_3$

Parallel Circuits:

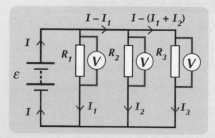

1) **current** is **split** at each **junction**, so: $I = I_1 + I_2 + I_3$

2) **same p.d.** across **all components** (remember that within a loop the e.m.f. equals the sum of individual p.d.s)

3) so, $V/R_{total} = V/R_1 + V/R_2 + V/R_3$

4) cancelling the Vs gives:

> $\dfrac{1}{R_{total}} = \dfrac{1}{R_1} + \dfrac{1}{R_2} + \dfrac{1}{R_3}$

...and there's an example on the next page to make sure you know what to do with all that...

Conservation of Charge & Energy in Circuits

Example:

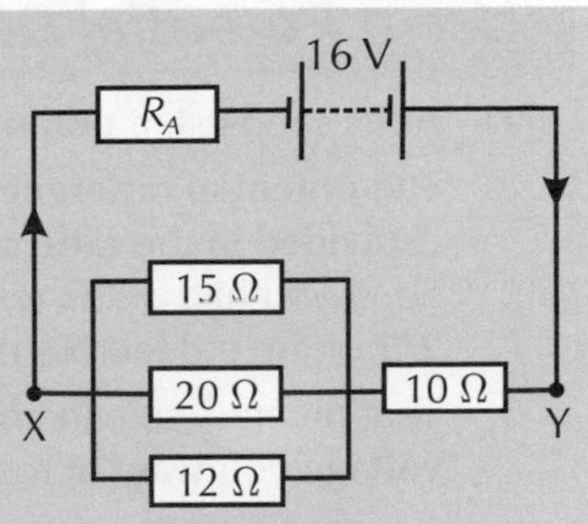

A battery with an e.m.f. of 16 V and negligible internal resistance is connected in a circuit as shown on the right.

a) Show that the group of resistors between X and Y could be replaced by a single resistor of resistance 15 Ω.

You can find the combined resistance of the 15 Ω, 20 Ω and 12 Ω resistors using: X

$1/R = 1/R_1 + 1/R_2 + 1/R_3 = 1/15 + 1/20 + 1/12 = 1/5 \Rightarrow R = 5\ \Omega$

So overall resistance between X and Y can be found by: $R = R_1 + R_2 = 5 + 10 = \textbf{15}\ \Omega$

b) If $R_A = 20\ \Omega$:
   i) calculate the potential difference across R_A.

Careful — there are a few steps here. You need the p.d. across R_A, but you don't know the current through it. So start there: total resistance in circuit = 20 + 15 = 35 Ω,
so current through R_A can be found using $I = V_{total}/R_{total} = 16/35$ A
then you can use $V = IR_A$ to find the p.d. across R_A: $V = 16/35 \times 20 = \textbf{9.1 V (to 2 s.f.)}$

   ii) calculate the current in the 15 Ω resistor.

You know the current flowing into the group of three resistors and out of it, but not through the individual branches. But you know that their combined resistance is 5 Ω from part a), so you can work out the p.d. across the group:

$V = IR = 16/35 \times 5 = 16/7$ V

The p.d. across the whole group is the same as the p.d. across each individual resistor, so you can use this to find the current through the 15 Ω resistor:

$I = V/R = (16/7) / 15 = \textbf{0.15 A (to 2 s.f.)}$

Q1 State Kirchhoff's first and second laws.

Q2 Find the current through and potential difference across each of two 5 Ω resistors when they are placed in a circuit containing a 5 V battery, and are wired: a) in series, b) in parallel.

Exam Question

Q1 For the circuit on the right:

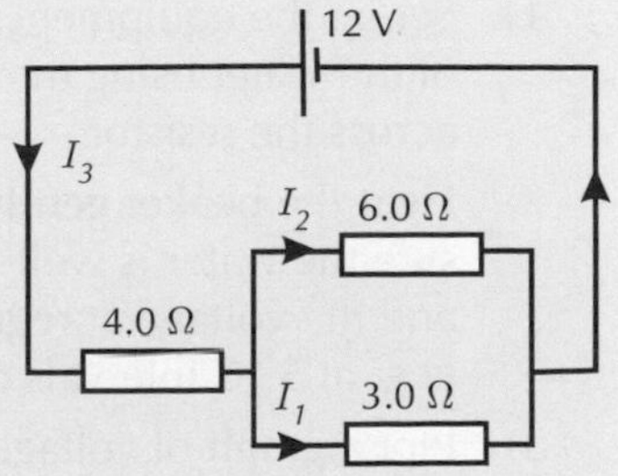

a) Calculate the total effective resistance of the three resistors in this combination. [2 marks]

b) Calculate the main current, I_3. [1 mark]

c) Calculate the potential difference across the 4 Ω resistor. [1 mark]

d) Calculate the potential difference across the parallel pair of resistors. [1 mark]

e) Calculate the currents I_1 and I_2. [2 marks]

Conservation of energy is really important — time for a nap I think...

V = IR is the formula you'll use most often in these questions. Make sure you know whether you're using it on the overall circuit, or just one specific component. It's amazingly easy to get muddled up — you've been warned.

The Potential Divider

It's probably best not to bring up this topic when you're having dinner with your in-laws — it's potentially quite divisive.

Use a **Potential Divider** to Get a **Fraction** of an **Input Voltage**

1) At its simplest, a **potential divider** is a circuit with a **voltage source** and a couple of **resistors** in series.

2) The **potential difference** of the voltage source (e.g. a power supply) is **divided** in the ratio of the **resistances**. As an equation: $$\frac{V_1}{V_2} = \frac{R_1}{R_2}$$
So, if you had a **2 Ω** resistor and a **3 Ω** resistor, you'd get **2/5** of the p.d. across the **2 Ω** resistor and **3/5** across the **3 Ω**.

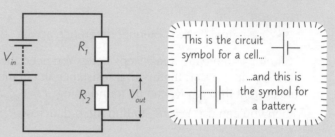
This rearranges to give $V_1/R_1 = V_2/R_2$. As $I = V/R$ this just means the current is the same through both resistors, which you know from page 70.

3) That means you can **choose** the **resistances** to get the **voltage** you **want** across one of them.

In the circuit shown, R_2 has $\frac{R_2}{R_1 + R_2}$ of the total resistance.

So:
$$V_{out} = \frac{R_2}{R_1 + R_2} V_{in}$$

E.g. if $V_{in} = 9\,V$ and you want V_{out} to be 6 V,

then you need: $\frac{R_2}{R_1 + R_2} = \frac{6}{9}$ which gives $R_2 = 2R_1$.

So you could have, say, **$R_1 = 100\,Ω$, $R_2 = 200\,Ω$**

This is the circuit symbol for a cell...
...and this is the symbol for a battery.

4) This circuit can be used for **calibrating voltmeters**, which have a **very high resistance**.

5) If you put something with a **relatively low resistance** across R_2 though, you start to run into **problems**. You've **effectively** got **two resistors** in **parallel**, which will **always** have a **total** resistance **less** than R_2. That means that V_{out} will be **less** than you've calculated, and will depend on what's connected across R_2. Hrrumph.

Add an **LDR** or **Thermistor** for a **Light** or **Temperature Sensor**

1) You can make a potential divider using a **light-dependent resistor** (LDR) or a **thermistor** (see page 63).

2) An **LDR** has a very **high resistance** in the **dark**, but a **lower resistance** in the **light**.

3) An **NTC thermistor** has a **high resistance** at **low temperatures**, but a much **lower resistance** at **high temperatures** (it varies in the opposite way to a normal resistor, only much more so).

4) This means V_{out} **varies** with light or heat, so you can make a potential divider that works as a light or heat **sensor**.

Here's a potential divider using an **NTC thermistor**.

Think about safety before you start. Keep the rest of the circuit as far away from the bunsen burner and the water bath as possible and make sure you waterproof the thermistor, e.g. by wrapping it in polythene.

You can investigate this circuit using the equipment shown on the right:

1) Set up the equipment as shown, then measure the **temperature** of the water using the **thermometer**, and record the **voltage** across the resistor.

2) **Heat** the beaker **gently** using the Bunsen burner (make sure the water is well-stirred), and record the temperature and the voltage at **regular intervals** over a **suitable range** (e.g. at 5 °C intervals over a range of 0-100 °C).

3) Plot a **graph** of voltage against temperature from your results.

This kind of circuit could form the basis of a digital thermometer (the graph of voltage against temperature would be the thermometer's **calibration curve**), or could form part of the circuit for a thermostat in a central heating system.

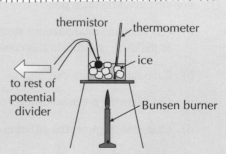

Pick your fixed resistor carefully — if its resistance is too high, V_{out} won't vary enough with temperature, and if it's too low V_{out} might vary over a bigger range than your voltmeter can handle.

The Potential Divider

A *Potentiometer* Uses a *Variable Resistor* to Give a *Variable Voltage*

1) A **potentiometer** has a **variable resistor** replacing R_1 and R_2 of the potential divider, but it uses the **same idea** (it's even sometimes **called** a potential divider just to confuse things).

2) You move a **slider** or turn a knob to **adjust** the **relative sizes** of R_1 and R_2. That way you can vary V_{out} from 0 V up to the input voltage, V_{in}.

3) This is dead handy when you want to be able to **change** a **voltage continuously**, like in the **volume control** of a stereo.

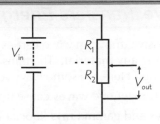

Here, V_{in} is replaced by the input signal (e.g. from a CD player) and V_{out} is the output to the amplifier and loudspeaker.

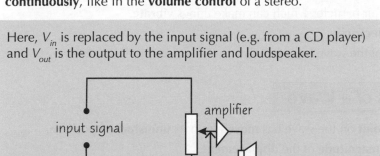

I've often wished bagpipes had a volume control. Or just an off switch.

Practice Questions

Q1 Write down the equation linking output p.d., input p.d., and component resistance for a potential divider circuit.

Q2 Draw the circuit diagram for a potential divider that works as a light sensor, where the output p.d. increases when the light level increases. How could you change the circuit so that the output p.d. decreases when the light level increases?

Q3 What is a potentiometer?

Exam Questions

Q1 Two resistors, A and B, are connected in series as shown in the circuit diagram. Resistor A has a resistance of 35 Ω and resistor B has a resistance of 45 Ω.

a) Given that the potential difference across resistor B is 6.75 V, calculate the potential difference across resistor A. [1 mark]

b) Calculate the input p.d. supplied by the battery. [1 mark]

c) Resistor A is removed, and replaced with a 75 Ω resistor. Calculate the new potential difference across resistor B. [1 mark]

Q2 Look at the circuit on the right.

a) Calculate the p.d. between A and B as shown by a high resistance voltmeter placed between the two points. [1 mark]

b) A 40 Ω resistor is now placed between points A and B. Calculate the p.d. across AB and the current flowing through the 40 Ω resistor. [4 marks]

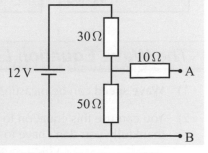

OI...YOU... [bang bang bang]... turn that potentiometer down...

Potentiometers come up a lot in experiments to do with electricity, so like them or not, you'd better get used to them. I can't stand the things myself, but then lab and me don't mix — it's all far too technical I'm afraid.

Wave Basics

Aaaah... waggling ropes about. It's all good clean fun as my mate Richard used to say...

A **Wave** Transfers **Energy** Away From Its **Source**

A **progressive** (moving) wave carries **energy** from one place to another **without transferring any material**. The transfer of energy is in the **same direction** as the wave is **travelling**. Here are some ways you can tell waves carry energy:

1) Electromagnetic waves cause things to **heat up**.
2) **X-rays** and **gamma rays** knock electrons out of their orbits, causing **ionisation**.
3) Loud **sounds** cause large oscillations in air particles which can make things **vibrate**.
4) **Wave power** can be used to **generate electricity**.

Since waves carry energy away, the **source** of the wave **loses energy**.

You Need to Know These **Bits** of a **Wave**

1) **Displacement**, *x*, metres — how far a **point** on the wave has **moved** from its **undisturbed position**.
2) **Amplitude**, *A*, metres — the **maximum magnitude** of the **displacement**.
3) **Wavelength**, λ, metres — the **length** of **one whole wave cycle**, e.g. from **crest** to **crest** or **trough** to **trough**.

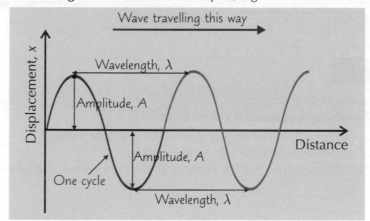

4) **Period**, *T*, seconds — the **time taken** for a **whole cycle** (vibration) to complete.
5) **Frequency**, *f*, hertz — the **number** of **cycles** (vibrations) **per second** passing a given **point**.
6) **Phase** — a measurement of the **position** of a certain **point** along the wave cycle.
7) **Phase difference** — the amount one wave lags behind another.

Phase and phase difference are measured in angles (in degrees or radians). See p.84.

The **Frequency** is the **Inverse** of the **Period**

$$\text{Frequency} = \frac{1}{\text{Period}} \qquad f = \frac{1}{T}$$

It's that simple.
Get the **units** straight: **1 Hz = 1 s^{-1}**.

The **Wave Equation** Links **Wave Speed, Frequency** and **Wavelength**

1) **Wave speed** can be measured just like the speed of anything else: $\Longrightarrow$

$$\text{Wave speed } (v) = \frac{\text{Distance } (d)}{\text{Time } (t)}$$

2) You can use this equation to derive the **wave equation** (but thankfully you don't have to do that, you just need to be able to use it).

$$\text{Speed of wave } (v) = \text{frequency } (f) \times \text{wavelength } (\lambda) \qquad v = f\lambda$$

*Remember, you're not measuring how fast a physical point (like one molecule of rope) moves. You're measuring how fast a point on the **wave pattern** moves.*

Wave Basics

Oscilloscopes Display Waves

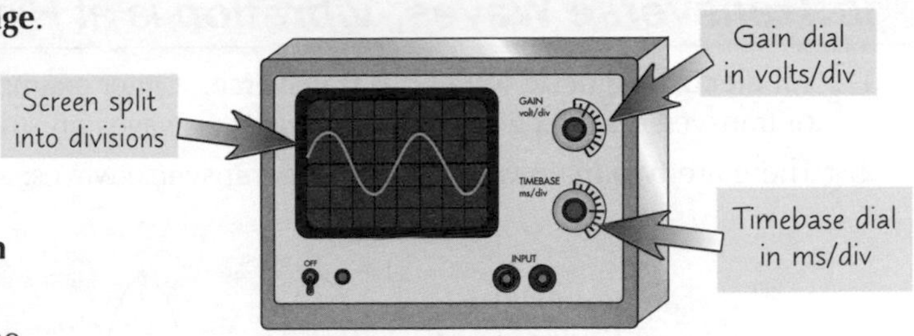

1) A cathode ray **oscilloscope** (CRO) measures **voltage**. It **displays** waves from a **signal generator** as a function of **voltage** over **time**.

2) The displayed wave is called a **trace**.

3) The screen is split into squares called **divisions**.

4) The vertical axis is in **volts**. The **volts per division** shown on this axis is controlled by the **gain dial**.

5) The horizontal axis is in **seconds** — also called the **timebase**. The **seconds per division** shown on this axis is controlled by the **timebase** dial.

6) You can alter the gain and timebase to make it **easy to read** off measurements.

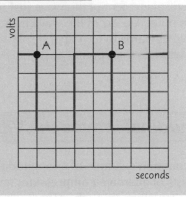

Screen split into divisions

Gain dial in volts/div

Timebase dial in ms/div

You Get Different Traces Depending on the Source

1) If you plug an **AC** (**alternating**) **supply** into an oscilloscope, you get a trace that goes up and down in a regular pattern — some of the time it's positive and some of the time it's negative.

2) A **microphone** converts **sound waves** into **electrical signals** which can be seen on an **oscilloscope**.

You Can Find Wave Frequency Using an Oscilloscope

Example: Find the frequency shown by the oscilloscope trace on the right. The timebase is set to 4.0 ms / div.

First calculate the period of the wave.
Point A to B is one cycle — which is **4** squares wide.

This means for one cycle it takes 4×4.0 ms = 16 ms.
So, the period $T = \textbf{16 ms}$.
Now, use $f = \frac{1}{T}$ to find the frequency:

$$f = \frac{1}{16 \times 10^{-3}} = \textbf{62.5 Hz} = \textbf{63 Hz (to 2 s.f.)}$$

volts

A   B

seconds

Practice Questions

Q1 Does a wave carry matter **or** energy from one place to another?

Q2 Give the units of frequency, displacement and amplitude.

Q3 Write down the wave equation.

Q4 What settings could you alter to make an oscilloscope wave trace easier to measure?

Exam Question

Q1 An oscilloscope has the gain set to 2.0 volts/div and a timebase set to 3.0 ms/div. It is displaying the trace of a wave that has a wave speed of 280 ms^{-1}.

volts/div

a) State the maximum voltage of the trace.   [1 mark]

b) Calculate the frequency of the wave.   [3 marks]

c) Calculate the wavelength of the wave.   [2 marks]

s/div

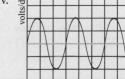

Hope you haven't phased out...

You should have met some of this stuff at GCSE, but it's all really important stuff. Make sure you know what all the waves terms (amplitude, frequency etc.) mean — otherwise the rest of the section is going sound like a confusing wavey mess...

Types of Wave

Get a long spring and have a go at making different waves. Or sit there beeping pretending to be a microwave.

In **Transverse Waves**, **Vibration** is at Right Angles to the **Direction** of Travel

1) All **electromagnetic waves** are **transverse**. Other examples of transverse waves are ripples on water or waves on strings.

2) There are **two** main ways of **drawing** transverse waves:

They can be shown as **graphs of displacement** against **distance along the path of the wave**.

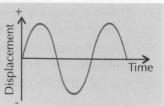

Or, they can be shown as graphs of **displacement against time** for a point as the wave passes.

3) Both sorts of graph often give the **same shape**, so make sure you check out the label on the **x-axis**. Displacements **upwards** from the centre line are given a **+ sign**. Displacements downwards are given a **– sign**.

4) You can work out what **direction** a point on a wave is moving in when given a snapshot of the wave.

Example: Look at the snapshot of the wave on the right. Which direction is point A on the wave moving in?

1) Look at which **direction** the wave is **travelling** in — here the wave is moving from **left** to **right**.

2) The displacement of the wave **just to the left** of point A is **greater** than point A's. So as the wave travels along, point A will need to move **upwards** to have that displacement. (If the displacement to the left was less than point A's, point A would need to move down.)

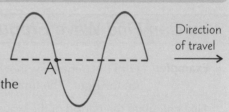

Direction of travel

In **Longitudinal Waves** the **Vibrations** are **Along** the Direction of Travel

The most **common** example of a **longitudinal wave** is **sound**. A sound wave consists of alternate **compressions** and **rarefactions** of the **medium** it's travelling through. (That's why sound can't go through a vacuum.) Some types of **earthquake shock waves** are also longitudinal.

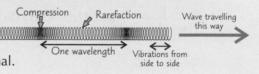

It's hard to **represent** longitudinal waves **graphically**. You'll usually see them plotted as **displacement** against **time**. These can be **confusing** though, because they look like a **transverse wave**.

Intensity is a Measure of How Much **Energy** a Wave is **Carrying**

1) When you talk about "**brightness**" for light or "**loudness**" for sound, what you really mean is **how much light** or **sound** energy hits your eyes or your ears **per second**.

2) The scientific measure of this is **intensity**.

Intensity is the **rate of flow** of **energy** per **unit area** at **right angles** to the **direction of travel** of the wave. It's measured in **Wm⁻²**.

$$\text{Intensity} = \frac{\text{Power}}{\text{Area}} \qquad I = \frac{P}{A}$$

Intensity is Proportional to **Amplitude Squared**

1) This comes from the fact that **intensity** is **proportional** to **energy**, and the energy of a wave depends on the square of the **amplitude**.

$$\text{Intensity} \propto (\text{Amplitude})^2$$

2) From this you can tell that for a **vibrating source** it takes four times as much energy to double the size of the vibrations.

Types of Wave

All *Electromagnetic (EM) Waves* Have Some *Properties* In Common

1) All EM waves travel in a **vacuum** at a **speed** of **3.00 × 10⁸ ms⁻¹** (to 3 s.f.), and at **slower** speeds in other media.

2) They are **transverse** waves consisting of **vibrating electric** and **magnetic fields**. The **electric** and **magnetic** fields are at **right angles** to each other and to the **direction of travel**.

3) Like all waves, EM waves can be **refracted** (p.82), **reflected** and **diffracted** (p.80-81) and can undergo **interference** (p.84). They also obey $v = f\lambda$ (v = velocity, f = frequency, λ = wavelength).

4) Like all progressive waves, progressive EM waves **carry energy**.

5) EM waves are transverse so, like all transverse waves, they can be **polarised** (see page 78).

Some *Properties Vary* Across the *EM Spectrum*

EM waves with different wavelengths behave differently in some respects. The spectrum is split into seven categories: **radio waves**, **microwaves**, **infrared**, **visible light**, **ultraviolet**, **X-rays** and **gamma rays**.

1) The longer the wavelength, the more **obvious** the wave characteristics — long radio waves diffract round hills.

2) **Energy** is directly proportional to **frequency**. **Gamma rays** have the **highest energy**; **radio waves** the **lowest**.

3) In general, the **higher** the **energy**, the more **dangerous** the wave — some can even cause **ionisation**.

Type	Approximate Wavelength /m	Penetration	Uses
Radio waves	10^{-1} — 10^{6}	Pass through matter.	Radio transmissions.
Microwaves	10^{-3} — 10^{-1}	Mostly pass through matter, but cause some heating.	Radar. Microwave cooking. TV transmissions.
Infrared (IR)	7×10^{-7} — 10^{-3}	Mostly absorbed by matter, causing it to heat up.	Heat detectors. Night vision cameras. Remote controls. Optical fibres.
Visible light	4×10^{-7} — 7×10^{-7}	Absorbed by matter, causing some heating.	Human sight. Optical fibres.
Ultraviolet (UV)	10^{-8} — 4×10^{-7}	Absorbed by matter. Slight ionisation.	Sunbeds. Security marks that show up under UV.
X-rays	10^{-13} — 10^{-8}	Mostly pass through matter, but cause ionisation as they pass.	To see damage to bones and teeth. Airport security scanners. To kill cancer cells.
Gamma rays	10^{-16} — 10^{-10}	Mostly pass through matter, but cause ionisation as they pass.	Irradiation of food. Sterilisation of medical instruments. To kill cancer cells.

Practice Questions

Q1 Draw a displacement-time graph for a point on a wave as the wave passes.

Q2 Describe the difference between the vibrations in a transverse wave and a longitudinal wave.

Q3 State the two types of field that make up an EM wave and describe the direction of their vibrations.

Q4 Name four properties that all electromagnetic waves have.

Q5 Name the main types of EM wave that make up the electromagnetic spectrum.

Q6 Which types of electromagnetic radiation have the highest and lowest energies?

Q7 What are the approximate wavelengths for: a) radio waves   b) microwaves?

Exam Question

Q1 a) A 10.0 W light beam is shone onto a screen with an area of 0.002 m². Calculate the intensity of the light beam on the screen. [1 mark]

b) The intensity of the light on the screen is increased until it is exactly triple the original beam intensity. Which of the following describes the amplitude of the light waves in the beam compared to their original amplitude?

A It is 3 times larger.   B It has halved.   C It is 9 times larger.   D It is √3 larger. [1 mark]

I've got UV hair...

No really I have, you just can't see it. Aaanyway... moving swiftly on. Loads of facts to learn on this page — and that's just what you have to do I'm afraid, sit and learn it then make sure you really know it. Not much fun, but there you go.

Polarisation of Waves

Light waves shake about all over the place. Polarisation is just getting rid of the directions that you don't want.

A *Polarised Wave* Only *Oscillates* in One Direction

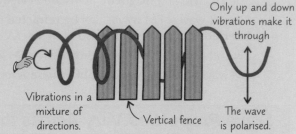

Only up and down vibrations make it through

Vibrations in a mixture of directions.

Vertical fence

The wave is polarised.

1) If you **shake a rope** to make a **wave** you can move your hand **up and down** or **side to side** or in a **mixture** of directions — it still makes a **transverse wave**.

2) But if you try to pass **waves in a rope** through a **vertical fence**, the wave will only get through if the **vibrations** are **vertical**. The fence filters out vibration in other directions. This is called **polarising** the wave.

3) The **plane** in which a wave **vibrates** is called the **plane of polarisation** — e.g. the rope wave was polarised in the **vertical** plane by the fence.

4) Polarising a wave so that it only oscillates in one direction is called **plane polarisation**.

5) Ordinary **light waves** are a mixture of **different directions** of **vibration**. (The things vibrating are electric and magnetic fields).

6) A **polarising filter** only transmits vibrations in one direction.

*A plane is a **flat surface** in 3D space.*

7) If you have two polarising filters at **right angles** to each other, then **no** light will get through.

8) Polarisation **can only happen** for **transverse** waves. The fact that you can polarise light is one **proof** that it's a transverse wave.

Investigating *Polarisation* of *Light* Using Two *Polarising Filters*

You can observe polarisation by shining unpolarised white light through two polarising filters.

1) Align the transmission axes of two **polarising filters** so they are both **vertical**. Shine unpolarised light on the first filter. Keep the position of the **first filter fixed** and **rotate** the second one.

2) Light that passes through the first filter will always be **vertically polarised**.

3) When the transmission axes of the two filters are **aligned**, **all** of the light that passes through the first filter also passes through the second.

4) As you rotate the second filter, the amount of light that passes through the second filter **varies**.

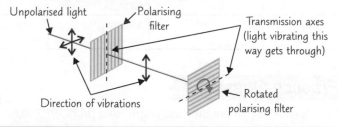

Unpolarised light

Polarising filter

Transmission axes (light vibrating this way gets through)

Direction of vibrations

Rotated polarising filter

Just like vectors, you can think of the transmission axis of the rotating filter as having a **vertical** and **horizontal** component. The **larger** the **vertical component**, the **more** vertically polarised light will pass through the filter.

5) As the second filter is rotated, **less** light will get through it as the **vertical** component of the second filter's transmission axis **decreases**. This means the **intensity** of the light getting through the second filter will gradually **decrease**.

6) When the two transmission axes are at **45°** to each other, the intensity will be **half** that getting through the first filter. When they're at **right angles** to each other **no** light will pass through — **intensity** is **0**.

7) As you continue turning, the intensity should then begin to **increase** once again.

8) When the two axes **realign** (after a 180° rotation), **all** the light will be able to pass through the second filter again.

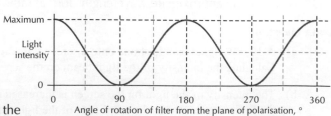

Maximum

Light intensity

0

0   90   180   270   360

Angle of rotation of filter from the plane of polarisation, °

You come across polarising filters more often than you'd think. For example, **3D films** use polarised light to create depth — the filters in each lens are at right angles to each other so each eye gets a slightly different picture. **Polaroid sunglasses** also use polarising filters — reflected light is partially polarised so the sunglasses block this out to help prevent glare.

Polarisation of Waves

You Can Also **Polarise Microwaves**

Polarising filters don't work on **microwaves** — their **wavelength** is too long. Instead, **metal grilles** (squares full of metal wires which are all aligned) are used to polarise them.

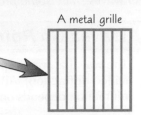

A metal grille

You can investigate the polarisation of microwaves using a **microwave transmitter** and a **microwave receiver** linked to a **voltmeter**.

1) Place a metal **grille** between the microwave **transmitter** and **receiver** as shown on the right. (Handily, microwave transmitters transmit **vertically polarised** microwaves, so you only need one metal grille.)

2) The intensity of microwaves passing through the grille is at a **maximum** when the direction of the vibration of the microwaves and the wires on the grille are at **right angles** to each other.

3) As you rotate the grille, the **intensity** of polarised microwaves able to pass through the grille **decreases**, so the reading on the voltmeter **decreases**.

4) When the wires of the metal grille are **aligned** with the direction of the polarised waves, **no signal** will be shown on the voltmeter.

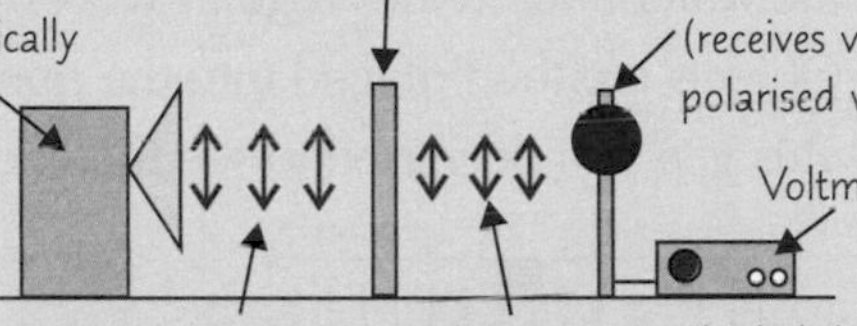

Microwave transmitter transmitting vertically polarised waves

Metal grille at right angle to direction of microwaves

Microwave receiver (receives vertically polarised waves)

Voltmeter

Polarised microwaves (direction of vibrations)

Microwaves with slightly reduced amplitudes

The **intensity** drops to **zero** when the wires are **aligned** with the direction of the microwaves, because the grille is **absorbing their energy**.

Make sure all of your electrical equipment is safely connected before you turn it on — microwave transmitters operate at very high voltages.

1) The vibrating electric field of the microwave **excites** electrons in the metal grille.

2) The energy of the incoming microwaves is **absorbed** and **re-emitted** in **all directions**.

3) Only a few of those re-emitted waves are vibrating in the **direction** of the microwave receiver.

4) The microwave **receiver** only receives microwaves in **one plane**, so even if the **re-emitted** wave travels towards to receiver, it might not be picked up.

5) When the wires and vibrations of the waves are **aligned**, **more** electrons are excited than when the grille and vibration of the waves are at right angles to each other — causing the drop in **intensity** that you see.

Practice Questions

Q1 What is plane polarisation?

Q2 Why can't you polarise sound waves?

Q3 Describe an experiment that shows visible light can be polarised.

Q4 Explain why the intensity of vertically polarised microwaves passing through a metal grille will drop to zero when the grille is aligned with the direction of polarisation.

Exam Question

Q1 Two polarising filters are placed on top of each other and held in front of a source of white unpolarised light.

a) No light can be seen through the filters. State the angle between the transmission axes of the two filters. [1 mark]

b) The filters are rotated so that the angle between their transmission axes is 45°. Describe the difference in the intensity of the light once it has passed through both filters compared to the light once it has only passed through the first filter. [1 mark]

c) Give one use of polarising filters. [1 mark]

Forget polarisation, I need a mental filter...

...to stop me talking rubbish all the time. Polarisation isn't too bad once you get your head around it. It's just a case of filtering out different directions of wave vibrations. Make sure you really know it though as you'll have to be able to explain how both the experiments for polarising light and microwaves work. Doesn't that sound like a barrel of laughs.

Diffraction and Reflection

All waves share some properties — they spread out (diffract), reflect off stuff and refract (more on that on p.82-83).

Waves Go **Round Corners** and **Spread out** of Gaps

The way that **waves spread out** as they come through a **narrow gap** or go round obstacles is called **diffraction**. **All** waves diffract, but it's not always easy to observe. The amount of diffraction depends on the **size of the gap** in comparison to the **wavelength** of the wave.

You Can Use a **Ripple Tank** to Investigate **Diffraction**

1) **Ripple tanks** are shallow tanks of water that you can generate a wave in.

2) This is done by an **oscillating paddle**, which continually dips into the water and creates regular waves with straight, parallel wave fronts.

3) Objects are then placed into the ripple tank to create a **barrier** with a **gap** in the middle of it.

4) This gap can be varied to see the effects this has on how the waves spread through the tank.

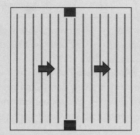

When the gap is **a lot bigger** than the **wavelength**, diffraction is **unnoticeable**.

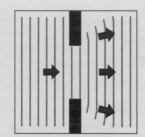

You get **noticeable diffraction** through a gap **several** wavelengths wide.

You get the **most** diffraction when the gap is **the same** size as the **wavelength**.

As the gap decreases, the diffraction becomes more noticeable until the gap becomes too small and the water waves cannot pass through it anymore. The waves are then **reflected** back on themselves.

When **sound** passes through a **doorway**, the **size of gap** and the **wavelength** are usually roughly **equal**, so **a lot of diffraction** occurs. That's why you have no trouble **hearing** someone through an **open door** to the next room, even if the other person is out of your **line of sight**. The reason that you can't **see** him or her is that when **light** passes through the doorway, it is passing through a **gap** around a **hundred million times bigger** than its wavelength — the amount of diffraction is **tiny**.

Demonstrate **Diffraction** in **Light** Using **Laser Light**

1) Diffraction in **light** can be demonstrated by shining a **laser light** through a very **narrow slit** onto a screen (see the next page). You can alter the amount of diffraction by changing the width of the slit.

2) You can do a similar experiment using a **white light** source instead of the laser (which is monochromatic) and a set of **colour filters**. The size of the slit can be kept constant while the **wavelength** is varied by putting different **colour filters** over the slit.

Warning. Use of coloured filters may result in excessive fun.

You Get a **Similar** Effect Around an Obstacle

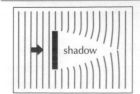

When a wave meets an **obstacle**, you get diffraction around the edges. Behind the obstacle is a '**shadow**', where the wave is blocked. The **wider** the obstacle compared with the wavelength of the wave, the less diffraction you get, and so the **longer** the shadow.

Diffraction and Reflection

With **Light Waves** you get a Pattern of **Light** and **Dark Fringes**

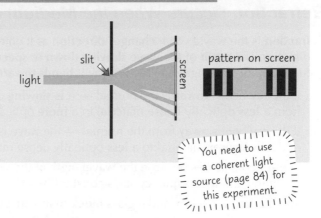

1) If the **wavelength** of a **light wave** is roughly similar to the size of the **aperture**, you get a **diffraction pattern** of light and dark fringes.

2) The pattern has a **bright central fringe** with alternating **dark and bright fringes** on either side of it.

3) The **narrower** the slit, the **wider** the diffraction pattern.

You need to use a coherent light source (page 84) for this experiment.

Waves Can Be **Reflected**

Reflection means the wave is **bounced back** when it **hits a boundary**. The **angle of incidence** always **equals** the angle of reflection.

You can show the reflection of water waves in a **ripple tank**.

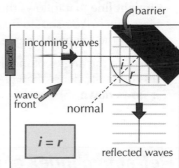

1) Set up the ripple tank so the oscillating paddle is creating **regular** waves with straight, **parallel** wave fronts. Place a **barrier** in the tank at an **angle** to the wave fronts.

2) The **angle** the incoming waves make with the **normal** to the barrier is called the **angle of incidence**, *i*.

3) You should see the waves **reflecting** off the barrier and travelling in a different direction to the way they arrived.

4) The angle between the **direction** of the **reflected waves** and the **normal** to the barrier is called the **angle of reflection**, *r*.

5) You can change the **angle of incidence** to see that the angle of **reflection** changes by the same amount. They are always **equal** to each other.

$i = r$

Practice Questions

Q1 What is diffraction?

Q2 For a long time some scientists argued that light couldn't be a wave because it did not seem to diffract. Suggest why they might have got this impression.

Q3 Sketch what happens when plane waves meet an obstacle about as wide as one wavelength.

Q4 In a ripple tank experiment, incident waves arrive at a barrier's surface at an angle of 30° to the normal. What is the angle between the incident waves and the reflected waves?

Exam Questions

Q1 A mountain lies directly between you and a radio transmitter. Explain, with the use of a diagram, why you can pick up long-wave radio broadcasts from the transmitter but not short-wave radio broadcasts. [3 marks]

Q2 Describe how you would use a ripple tank to investigate how the wavelength of a wave and the size of the gap a wave travels through relates to the amount of diffraction which occurs. Comment on when maximum diffraction will be seen. [3 marks]

Even hiding behind a mountain, you can't get away from long-wave radio...

Unfortunately "Bay FM" don't transmit using long wave radio. So as I'm giving the singing-in-the-car performance of my life, I go over a hill and the signal cuts out. Where's diffraction when I need it then hmm? How will I ever become famous? Diffraction crops up again in stuff like quantum physics so make sure you really understand it.

Refraction and Refractive Index

The stuff on the next two pages explains why your legs look short in a swimming pool.

Refraction Occurs When the Medium a Wave is Travelling in Changes

Refraction is the way a wave **changes direction** as it enters a **different medium**. The change in direction is a result of the wave **slowing down** or **speeding up**. You can tell if the wave is speeding up or slowing down by the way it **bends towards** or **away** from the normal.

1) If the ray bends **towards** the normal — it is **slowing** down. The ray is going from a **less** optically dense material to a **more** optically dense material.

2) If the ray bends **away** from the normal — the wave is **speeding up**. It is going from an optically **denser** material to a **less** optically dense material.

Knowing there's biscuits also causes a change in speed

3) The speed changes because the **wavelength** of the wave is changing and the **frequency** stays **constant** ($v = f\lambda$).

4) You can use a **ray box** and a **glass block** to investigate refraction:

1) Place a glass block on a piece of paper and draw around it.

2) Use the ray box to shine a beam of light into the glass block. Turn off any other lights so you can see the path of the light beam through the block clearly.

3) **Trace** the path of the **incoming** and **outgoing** beams of light either side of the block.

4) Remove the block and join up the two paths you've drawn with a **straight line** that follows the path the light beam took through the glass block. You should be able to see from your drawing how the path of the ray **bent** when entering and leaving the block.

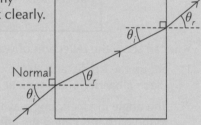

5) Measure the angles of incidence (θ_i) and refraction (θ_r) where the light enters and exits the block. Air is **less** optically dense than glass, so as the light **enters** the glass block it **bends towards** the normal ($\theta_i > \theta_r$) as it **slows down**. The beam should **bend away** from the normal as it **exits** the block ($\theta_r > \theta_i$) and **speeds up**.

The Refractive Index of a Material Measures How Much It Slows Down Light

Light goes fastest in a **vacuum**. It **slows down** in other materials, because it **interacts** with the particles in them. The more **optically dense** a material is, the more light **slows down** when it enters it.

The **absolute refractive index** of a material, *n*, is the **ratio** between the **speed of light** in a **vacuum**, *c*, and the speed of light in that **material, v**.

$$n = \frac{c}{v}$$

$c = 3.00 \times 10^8 \, \text{ms}^{-1}$.

The speed of light in air is only a tiny bit smaller than c. So you can assume the refractive index of air is 1.

Snell's Law uses Angles to Calculate the Refractive Index

When a light ray passes across a boundary between two materials: $\boxed{n \sin \theta = \text{constant}}$

Where *n* is the refractive index of the material light travels in, and *θ* is the angle the light ray makes with the normal of the boundary.

This means that for a light ray at a boundary between two materials, **n sin θ** must be the same on either side. This can be written nicely as **Snell's Law**:

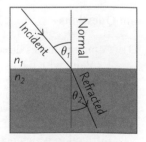

$$\boxed{n_1 \sin \theta_1 = n_2 \sin \theta_2}$$

where n_1 is the refractive index of the first material, θ_1 is the angle of incidence, n_2 is the refractive index of the second material and θ_2 is the angle of refraction.

You can use a device called a **refractometer** to accurately measure the refractive index of a material. The machine shines a beam of light at the sample. You then view the refracted beam through a **microscope** and measure its angle of refraction.

You'll only get given the 'n sin θ = constant' equation in the exam, so make sure you remember what that equation actually tells you — that $n_1 \sin \theta_1 = n_2 \sin \theta_2$ at any boundary.

Refraction and Refractive Index

When the Angle of *Refraction* is a *Right Angle*, the Angle of *Incidence* is *Critical*

When light **goes from** an optically dense material into an optically
less dense material (e.g. glass to air), interesting things can start to happen.

Shine a ray of light at a **glass to air** boundary, then gradually **increase** the angle of
incidence. As you increase the angle of incidence, the angle of **refraction** gets closer
and closer to **90°**. Eventually the angle of incidence, θ_i reaches a **critical angle C** for
which the angle of refraction, $\theta_r = 90°$. The light is refracted **along the boundary**.

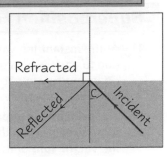

At angles of incidence **greater than** C, refraction is **impossible**. That means **all** the
light is reflected back into the material. This effect is called **total internal reflection**.

For light hitting a **material-to-air boundary**
(assuming the material is more optically **dense**) at
the critical angle, **Snell's law** simplifies to become:

$$\sin C = \frac{1}{n}$$

This happens because $n_{air} = 1$ and $\sin(90°) = 1$.
n is the refractive index of the material.

You can Investigate *Critical Angles* and *Total Internal Reflection* with *Glass Blocks*

1) Shine a light ray into the **curved face** of a semi-circular glass block so that it always enters at **right angles**
   to the edge — this means the ray won't **refract** as it enters the block, just when it leaves from the straight edge.

2) Vary the angle of **incidence**, θ_i, until the light beam refracts
   so much that it exits the block along the **straight edge**. This
   angle of incidence is the **critical angle**, **C**, for glass-air boundary.

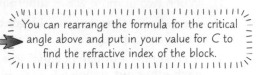

You can rearrange the formula for the critical
angle above and put in your value for C to
find the refractive index of the block.

3) If you increase the angle of incidence so it's **greater** than C,
   you'll find the ray is reflected from the straight edge of the block.

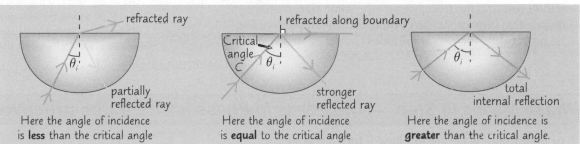

Here the angle of incidence
is **less** than the critical angle

Here the angle of incidence
is **equal** to the critical angle

Here the angle of incidence is
greater than the critical angle.

Practice Questions

Q1 What happens to the wavelength of light at an air-water boundary?
Q2 Why does light go fastest in a vacuum and slow down in other media?
Q3 Describe an experiment you could do to determine the critical angle of a boundary between a material and air.

Exam Questions

Q1 a) Light travels in diamond at 1.24×10^8 ms^{-1}. What is the refractive index of diamond? [1 mark]

b) Calculate the angle of refraction if light strikes a facet of a diamond ring at an angle of 50°
   to the normal of the air/diamond boundary. [2 marks]

Q2 An adjustable underwater spotlight is placed on the floor of an aquarium tank. When the light points upwards at a
   steep angle a beam comes through the surface of the water into the air, and the tank is dimly lit. When the spotlight
   is placed at a shallower angle, no light comes up through the water surface, and the tank is brightly lit.

a) Explain what is happening. [2 marks]

b) It is found that the beam into the air disappears when the spotlight is pointed at any angle
   of less than 41.25° to the floor. Calculate the refractive index of water. [2 marks]

Critical angles are never happy...

*Total internal reflection doesn't sound like the most riveting subject, but it's super useful. Optical fibres wouldn't work
without it, and we use them for all sorts of things — broadband connections, telephone cables, making things sparkley...*

Superposition and Coherence

When two waves get together, it can be either really impressive or really disappointing.

Superposition *Happens When* Two *or* More *Waves* Pass Through *Each Other*

1) At the **instant** the waves **cross**, the **displacements** due to each wave **combine**. Then **each wave** goes on its merry way. You can **see** this if **two pulses** are sent **simultaneously** from each end of a rope.

2) The **principle of superposition** says that when two or more **waves cross**, the **resultant** displacement equals the **vector sum** of the **individual** displacements.

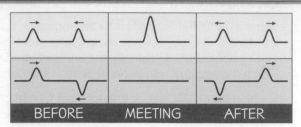

BEFORE   MEETING   AFTER

"Superposition" means "one thing on top of another thing". You can use the same idea in reverse — a complex wave can be separated out mathematically into several simple sine waves of various sizes.

Interference *can be* Constructive *or* Destructive

1) When two or more waves **superpose** with each other, the effect is called **interference**.

2) A **crest** plus a **crest** gives a **bigger crest**. A **trough** plus a **trough** gives a **bigger trough**. These are both examples of **constructive interference**.

3) A **crest** plus a **trough** of **equal size** gives... **nothing**. The two displacements **cancel each other out** completely. This is called **destructive interference**.

4) If the **crest** and the **trough** aren't the **same size**, then the destructive interference **isn't total**. For the interference to be **noticeable**, the two **amplitudes** should be **nearly equal**.

Graphically, you can superimpose waves by adding the individual displacements at each point along the x-axis, and then plotting them.

In Phase *Means In* Step — *Two Points* In Phase *Interfere* Constructively

1) Two points on a wave are **in phase** if they are both at the **same point** in the **wave cycle**. Points in phase have the **same displacement** and **velocity**.

2) On the graph on the right, points **A** and **B** are **in phase**; points **A** and **C** are **out of phase**.

3) It's mathematically **handy** to show one **complete cycle** of a wave as an **angle of 360° (2π radians)**.

4) **Two points** with a **phase difference** of **zero** or a **multiple of 360°** are **in phase**.

5) **Points** with a **phase difference** of **odd-number multiples** of **180° (π radians)** are **exactly out of phase**.

6) You can also talk about two **different waves** being **in phase**. **In practice** this happens because **both** waves came from the **same oscillator**. In **other** situations there will nearly always be a **phase difference** between two waves.

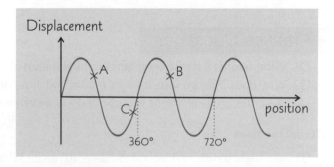

Displacement

position

360°   720°

To Get Interference Patterns *the* Two Sources *Must Be* Coherent

Interference **still happens** when you're observing waves of **different wavelength** and **frequency** — but it happens in a **jumble**. In order to get clear **interference patterns**, the two or more sources must be **coherent**.

Two sources are **coherent** if they have the **same wavelength** and **frequency** and a **fixed phase difference** between them.

In exam questions at AS, the 'fixed phase difference' is almost certainly going to be zero. The two sources will be in phase.

Superposition and Coherence

Constructive or Destructive Interference Depends on the Path Difference

1) Whether you get **constructive** or **destructive** interference at a **point** depends on how **much further one wave** has travelled than the **other wave** to get to that point (assuming the sources are coherent and in phase).

2) The **amount** by which the path travelled by one wave is **longer** than the path travelled by the other wave is called the **path difference**.

3) At **any point an equal distance** from both sources you will get **constructive interference**. You also get constructive interference at any point where the **path difference** is a **whole number of wavelengths**. At points where the path difference is an odd number of **half wavelengths**, the waves arrive **out of phase** and you get **destructive interference**.

Constructive interference occurs when:

$$\text{path difference} = n\lambda \quad \text{(where } n \text{ is an integer)}$$

Destructive interference occurs when:

$$\text{path difference} = \frac{(2n+1)\lambda}{2} = (n + \tfrac{1}{2})\lambda$$

You Can Observe Interference With Sound Waves

1) Connect two **speakers** to the same oscillator (so they're **coherent** and **in phase**) and place them in line with each other.

2) Walk slowly across the room in front of them.

3) You will hear varying volumes of sound. At the points where the sound is **loudest**, the **path difference** is a **whole** wavelength.

4) The sound will be quietest at points where the path difference is an **odd** number of **half wavelengths**.

Loud	Path diff = λ
Quiet	Path difference = $\frac{\lambda}{2}$
Loud	No path difference
Quiet	Path difference = $\frac{\lambda}{2}$
Loud	Path diff = λ

You may still hear some sound at the quietest points due to sound being reflected off walls and around the room.

Practice Questions

Q1 What is the principle of superposition?

Q2 What happens when a crest of one wave meets a slightly smaller trough of another wave?

Q3 If two points on a wave have a phase difference of 1440°, are they in phase?

Q4 If there was a path difference of 5λ between two in phase waves, what kind of interference would occur?

Exam Questions

Q1 a) Two wave sources are coherent. Explain what this means. [2 marks]

b) Explain why you might have difficulty in observing interference patterns in an area affected by two waves from two sources even though the two sources are coherent. [1 mark]

Q2 Two waves from coherent sources meet and interfere. Which row of the table shows the correct type of interference that would occur with the stated phase and path difference? [1 mark]

	Phase Difference	Path Difference	Type of Interference
A	180°	λ	Constructive
B	180°	$\lambda/2$	Constructive
C	360°	λ	Destructive
D	360°	$\lambda/2$	Constructive

Learn this and you'll be in a super position to pass your exam... ...I'll get my coat.

A few crucial concepts here: a) interference can be constructive or destructive, b) you get constructive interference when the path difference is a whole number of wavelengths (for sources in phase), c) the sources must be coherent.

Two-Source Interference

Yeah, I know, fringe spacing doesn't really sound like a Physics topic — just trust me on this one, OK.

Demonstrating Two-Source Interference in *Water* and *Sound* Waves is Easy

1) It's **easy** to demonstrate **two-source interference** for either **sound** or **water** waves because they've got **wavelengths** of a handy **size** that you can **measure**.

2) You need **coherent** sources, which means the **wavelength** and **frequency** have to be the **same**. The trick is to use the **same oscillator** to drive **both sources**. For **water**, one **vibrator drives two dippers**. For sound, **one oscillator** is connected to **two loudspeakers**. (See diagram on page 85.)

Demonstrating *Two-Source* Interference for *EM Radiation* is Harder

Light is more difficult to demonstrate two-source interference with — you can either use **two coherent light sources**, or use a single **laser** and shine it through **two slits**... clever, huh. It's called **Young's double-slit experiment**, and you need to learn it...

1) Laser light is **coherent** and **monochromatic** (there's only **one wavelength** present).

2) The slits have to be about the same size as the wavelength of the laser light so that it is **diffracted** — then the light from the slits acts like **two coherent point sources**.

3) You get a pattern of light and dark **fringes**, depending on whether constructive or destructive **interference** is taking place.

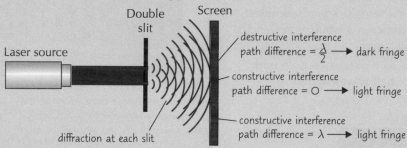

4) Thomas Young — the first person to do this experiment (with a lamp rather than a laser) — came up with an **equation** to **work out** the **wavelength** of the **light** from this experiment (see p.87).

5) To find the wavelength, you'll need to measure the **fringe spacing** — the distance from the **centre** of one **minimum** to the centre of the next minimum (or from one **maximum** centre to the next maximum centre).

6) The **fringes** are so **tiny** that it's very hard to get an accurate value for their **spacing** (*x*). It's easier to measure across **several fringes** and then divide by the number of **fringe spacings** between them. Doing this helps to lower the **percentage error** — see p.8 for more about this.

You Can Do a *Similar* Experiment with *Microwaves*

1) To see interference patterns with **microwaves**, you can **replace** the laser and slits with two microwave **transmitter cones** attached to the **same** signal generator.

2) You also need to replace the screen with a microwave **receiver probe** (like the one used in the stationary waves experiment on page 91).

3) If you move the probe along the path of the green arrow, you'll get an **alternating pattern** of **strong** and **weak** signals — just like the light and dark fringes on the screen.

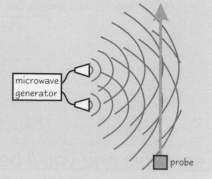

Two-Source Interference

The fringe spacing (**x**), wavelength (**λ**), spacing between slits (**a**) and the distance from slits to screen (**D**) are all related by **Young's double-slit formula**, which works for all waves when a << D.

Fringe Spacing, $x = \dfrac{\lambda D}{a}$

a has to be **much** smaller than *D* so you can use trigonometry to find this equation — including a small angle approximation of sin θ ≈ θ. Thankfully, you don't need to derive this equation.

Since the wavelength of light is so small you can see from the formula that a high ratio of **D / a** is needed to make the fringe spacing **big enough to see**.
You can rearrange the equation to **calculate the wavelength** of light. ➡️

$\lambda = \dfrac{ax}{D}$

Always check your fringe spacing.

Young's Experiment was Evidence for the Wave Nature of Light

1) Towards the end of the **17th century**, two important **theories of light** were published — one by Isaac Newton and the other by a chap called Huygens. **Newton's** theory suggested that light was made up of tiny particles, which he called "**corpuscles**". And **Huygens** put forward a theory using **waves**.

2) The **corpuscular theory** could explain **reflection** and **refraction**, but **diffraction** and **interference** are both **uniquely** wave properties. If it could be **shown** that light showed interference patterns, that would help settle the argument once and for all.

3) **Young's** double-slit experiment (over 100 years later) provided the necessary evidence. It showed that light could both **diffract** (through the narrow slits) and **interfere** (to form the interference pattern on the screen).

Of course, this being Physics, nothing's ever simple — give it another 100 years or so and the debate would be raging again.

Practice Questions

Q1 In Young's double-slit experiment, why do you get a bright fringe at a point equidistant from both slits?

Q2 Write down the formula you'd use to calculate the wavelength of light in Young's double-slit experiment.

Q3 What does Young's double-slit experiment show about the nature of light?

Exam Questions

Q1 a) The diagram on the right shows waves from two coherent light sources, S_1 and S_2.
Sketch the interference pattern, marking on constructive and destructive interference. [2 marks]

b) In practice if interference is to be observed, S_1 and S_2 must be slits in a screen behind which there is a source of laser light. Explain why this is so. [2 marks]

Q2 In an experiment to study sound interference, two loudspeakers are connected to an oscillator emitting sound at 1320 Hz and set up as shown in the diagram below. They are 1.5 m apart and 7 m away from the line AC. A listener moving from A to C hears minimum sound at A and C and maximum sound at B.
(You may assume that Young's double-slit formula can be used in this calculation.)

Oscillator ◁ 1.5m —7m— A B C

a) Calculate the wavelength of the sound waves if the speed of sound in air is taken to be 330 ms⁻¹. [1 mark]

b) Calculate the separation of points A and C. [2 marks]

I used to have a ridiculous fringe spacing...

... thankfully I stopped trying to cut my own hair. Seriously, leave it to the professionals. Be careful when you're calculating the fringe spacing by averaging over several fringes. Don't just divide by the number of bright lines. Ten bright lines will only have nine fringe-widths between them, not ten. It's an easy mistake to make, but you have been warned.

Diffraction Gratings

What could possibly be more exciting than shining a laser through two slits? Shining a laser through more than two slits of course. Jeez, ask a stupid question...

Interference Patterns Get **Sharper** When You Diffract Through **More Slits**

1) You can repeat **Young's double-slit** experiment (see p.86) with **more than two equally spaced** slits. You get basically the **same shaped** pattern as for two slits — but the **bright bands** are **brighter** and **narrower** and the **dark areas** between are **darker**.

2) When **monochromatic light** (one wavelength) is passed through a **grating** with **hundreds** of slits per millimetre, the interference pattern is **really sharp** because there are so **many beams reinforcing** the **pattern**.

3) Sharper fringes make for more **precise** measurements as they are easier to tell apart and so are **easier** to measure.

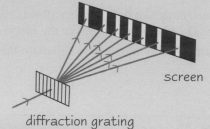

screen

diffraction grating

You can **Measure** the **Wavelength** of Light using a **Diffraction Grating**

1) For monochromatic light, all of the maxima are sharp lines. (It's different for white light — see the next page).

2) This means the distance between the maxima can be easily measured (**fringe width**).

3) There's a line of **maximum brightness** at the centre called the **zero order** line.

4) The lines just **either side** of the central one are called **first order lines**. The **next pair out** are called **second order** lines and so on.

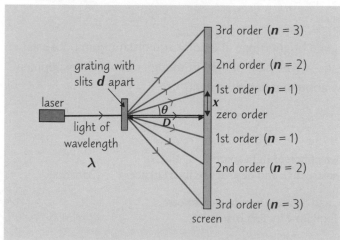

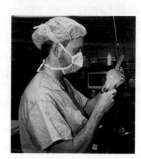

Graham's attempt to measure the wavelength of light was proving to be less than successful.

5) Using the **fringe width**, *x*, and the distance to the screen, *D*, the angle the 1st order fringe makes with the zero order line can be calculated using **small angle approximations**.

$$\tan \theta \approx \theta \text{ and } \tan \theta = \frac{x}{D}, \text{ so } \theta \approx \frac{x}{D}$$

6) The slit separation, *d*, for the diffraction grating is given.

7) If the grating has *N* slits per metre, then the slit separation, *d*, is just $1/N$ metres.

8) If you know the slit separation, *d*, what order maximum you're observing, *n*, and the angle between this maximum and the incident light, *θ*, you can find the **wavelength** of the incident light. $\longrightarrow$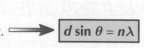

You don't need to know this equation unless you're doing A level Physics, but it's useful for understanding the experiment (which you do need to know) and how the wavelength affects the diffraction pattern.

Diffraction Gratings

You can Draw General Conclusions from d sin θ = nλ

1) If λ is **bigger**, **sin θ** is **bigger**, and so θ is **bigger**. This means that the larger the **wavelength**, the more the pattern will **spread out**.

2) If **d** is **bigger**, **sin θ** is **smaller**. This means that the **coarser** the **grating**, the **less** the pattern will **spread out**.

3) Values of **sin θ** greater than **1** are **impossible**. So if for a certain **n** you get a result of **more than 1** for **sin θ** you know that that order **doesn't exist**.

Shining White Light Through a Diffraction Grating Produces Spectra

1) **White light** is really a **mixture** of **colours**. If you **diffract** white light through a **grating** then the patterns due to **different wavelengths** within the white light are **spread out** by **different** amounts.

2) Each **order** in the pattern becomes a **spectrum**, with **red** on the **outside** and **violet** on the **inside**. The **zero order maximum** stays **white** because all the wavelengths just pass straight through.

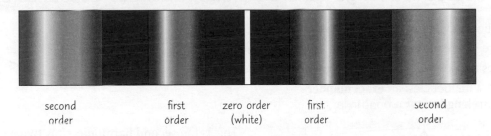

| second order | first order | zero order (white) | first order | second order |

Astronomers and chemists often need to study spectra to help identify elements. They use diffraction gratings rather than prisms because they're **more accurate**.

Practice Questions

Q1 What is the formula for finding the wavelength of light incident on a diffraction grating?

Q2 Why do more slits in a diffraction grating lead to a sharper diffraction pattern?

Q3 What equation is used to find the angle between the nth order maximum and the incident beam for a diffraction grating interference pattern?

Exam Questions

Q1 Yellow laser light of wavelength 6.00×10^{-7} m is transmitted through a diffraction grating of 4.0×10^5 lines per metre.

a) State the angle to the normal where the first and second order bright lines are seen. [4 marks]

b) State whether there is a fifth order line. Explain your answer. [1 mark]

Q2 Visible, monochromatic light is transmitted through a diffraction grating of 3.70×10^5 lines per metre. The first order maximum is at an angle of 14.2° to the incident beam.

Calculate the wavelength of the incident light. [2 marks]

Ooooooooooooo — pretty patterns...

Yes, it's the end of another beautiful topic. Three important points for you to take away — the more slits you have, the sharper the image, monochromatic light leads to sharp fringes and one lovely equation to get to know. Make sure you get everything in this topic — there's some good stuff waiting in the next one and I wouldn't want you to be distracted.

Stationary (Standing) Waves

Stationary waves are waves that... er... stand still... well, not still exactly... I mean, well... they don't go anywhere... um...

You get Stationary Waves When a **Progressive Wave** is **Reflected** at a **Boundary**

A stationary wave is the **superposition** of **two progressive waves** with the **same wavelength**, moving in **opposite directions**.

1) Unlike progressive waves, **no energy** is transmitted by a stationary wave.

2) You can demonstrate stationary waves by attaching a **vibration transducer** at one end of a **stretched string** with the other end fixed. The transducer is given a wave frequency by a **signal generator** and creates that wave by vibrating the string.

3) The wave generated by the vibration transducer is **reflected** back and forth.

4) For most frequencies the resultant **pattern** is a **jumble**. However, if you alter the **signal generator** so the **transducer** produces an **exact number of waves** in the time it takes for a wave to get to the **end** and **back again**, then the **original** and **reflected** waves **reinforce** each other.

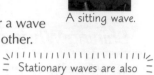
A sitting wave.

5) At these **"resonant frequencies"** you get a **stationary wave** where the **pattern doesn't move** — it just sits there, bobbing up and down. Happy, at peace with the world...

Stationary waves are also known as standing waves.

Stationary Waves in **Strings** Form **Oscillating "Loops"** Separated by **Nodes**

1) Each particle vibrates at **right angles** to the string.

2) **Nodes** are where the **amplitude** of the vibration is **zero**.

3) **Antinodes** are points of **maximum amplitude**.

4) At resonant frequencies, an **exact number** of **half wavelengths** fits onto the string.

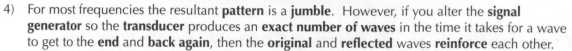

The standing wave above is vibrating at the **lowest possible** resonant frequency (the **fundamental mode of vibration** — also called the **first harmonic**). It has **one "loop"** with a **node at each end**.

This is the **second harmonic**. It is **twice** the **fundamental mode of vibration**. There are two **"loops"** with a **node** in the **middle** and **one at each end**.

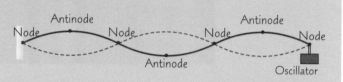

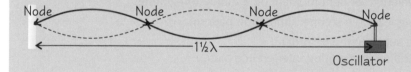

The **third harmonic** is **three times** the fundamental mode of vibration. **1½ wavelengths** fit on the string.

The **Notes** Played by **Stringed** and **Wind Instruments** are Stationary Waves

Transverse stationary waves form on the strings of **stringed instruments** like **violins** and **guitars**. Your finger or the bow sets the **string vibrating** at the point of contact. Waves are sent out in **both directions** and **reflected** back at both ends.

Longitudinal Stationary Waves Form in a **Wind Instrument** or Other Air **Column**

1) If a source of sound is placed at the open end of a flute, piccolo, oboe or other column of air, there will be some **frequencies** for which **resonance** occurs and a stationary wave is set up.

2) If the instrument has a **closed end**, a **node** will form there. You get the lowest resonant frequency when the length, *l*, of the pipe is a **quarter wavelength**.

$$l = \frac{\lambda}{4}$$

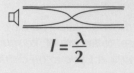
$$l = \frac{\lambda}{2}$$

3) **Antinodes** form at the **open ends** of pipes. If both ends are open, you get the lowest resonant frequency when the length, *l*, of the pipe is a **half wavelength**.

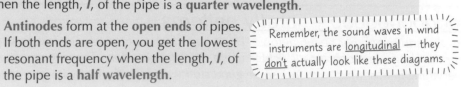
Remember, the sound waves in wind instruments are longitudinal — they don't actually look like these diagrams.

Stationary (Standing) Waves

You can Demonstrate Stationary Waves with Microwaves

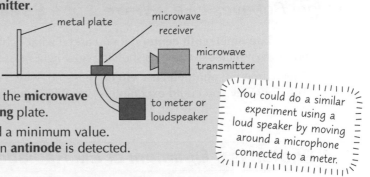

1) Microwaves are produced by a **microwave transmitter**.
2) They are **reflected** off a metal reflecting plate back towards the transmitter.
3) The reflected and incoming waves interfere and set up **stationary waves**.
4) You can find the **nodes** and **antinodes** by moving the **microwave receiver** between the **transmitter** and the **reflecting** plate.
5) Whenever a **node** is detected, the meter will read a minimum value. The meter will show a **maximum** reading when an **antinode** is detected.

You could do a similar experiment using a loud speaker by moving around a microphone connected to a meter.

You can Use Stationary Waves to Measure the Speed of Sound

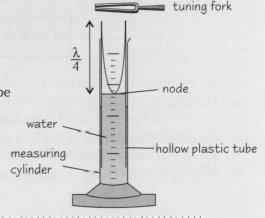

1) You can create a closed-end pipe by placing a **hollow tube** into a measuring cylinder of water.
2) Choose a tuning fork and note down the frequency of sound it produces (it'll be stamped on the side of it).
3) Gently tap the tuning fork and hold it just above the hollow tube. The sound waves produced by the fork travel down the tube and get reflected (and form a **node**) at the air/water surface.
4) Move the tube up and down until you find the **shortest distance** between the top of the tube and the water level that the sound from the fork **resonates** at (when the sound is at its loudest).
5) Just like with any closed pipe, this distance is a **quarter** of the **wavelength** of the stationary sound wave.
6) Once you know the frequency and wavelength of the stationary sound wave, you can work out the speed of sound (in air), v, using the equation $v = f\lambda$.

The antinode of the wave actually forms slightly above the top of the tube. You'd add an 'end correction value' on to take this into account, but you don't need to worry about it.

Practice Questions

Q1 How do stationary waves form?

Q2 At four times the first harmonic, how many half wavelengths fit on a violin string?

Q3 Describe an experiment to find the speed of sound in air using stationary waves.

Exam Questions

Q1 a) A stationary wave of three times the first harmonic is formed on a stretched string of length 1.2 m. Sketch a diagram showing the form of the wave. [2 marks]

b) Calculate the wavelength of the stationary wave. [1 mark]

c) Explain how the amplitude varies along the string. How is that different from the amplitude of a progressive wave? [2 marks]

Q2 A stationary wave microwave experiment is set up, using microwaves of 1.00 GHz. At a certain position x, the meter connected to the microwave receiver reads 0.00. The receiver is moved 15.0 cm along the line of the stationary wave until the meter once again reads 0.00. Calculate the speed at which the microwaves are travelling. [4 marks]

CGP — putting the FUN back in FUNdamental mode of vibration...

Resonance was a big problem for the Millennium Bridge in London. The resonant frequency of the bridge was roughly normal walking pace, so as soon as people started using it they set up a huge stationary wave. An oversight, I feel...

Light — Wave or Particle

*You probably already thought light was a bit weird — but oh no... being a wave that travels at the fastest
speed possible isn't enough for light — it has to go one step further and act like a particle too...*

Light Behaves Like a **Wave**... or a **Stream of Particles**

1) In the **late nineteenth century**, if you asked what light was, scientists would happily show
   you lots of nice experiments showing how light must be a **wave** (see Module 4: Section 2).

2) Then came the **photoelectric effect** (p.94-95), which mucked up everything.
   The only way you could explain this was if light acted as a **particle** — called a **photon**.

A **Photon** is a **Quantum** of **EM Radiation**

1) When Max Planck was investigating **black body radiation** (don't worry — you don't need to know
   about that right now), he suggested that **EM waves** can **only** be **released** in **discrete packets**, called
   quanta. A single packet of **EM radiation** is called a **quantum**.

   The **energy carried** by one of these **wave-packets** had to be:

$$E = hf = \frac{hc}{\lambda}$$

   where h = Planck constant = 6.63×10^{-34} Js,
   f = frequency (Hz), λ = wavelength (m) and
   c = speed of light in a vacuum = 3.00×10^{8} ms^{-1}

2) So, the **higher** the **frequency** of the electromagnetic radiation, the more **energy** its wave-packets carry.

3) **Einstein** went **further** by suggesting that **EM waves** (and the energy they carry) can only **exist** in
   discrete packets. He called these wave-packets **photons**.

4) He believed that a photon acts as a **particle**, and will either transfer **all** or **none** of its energy when
   interacting with another particle, e.g. an electron.

5) Photons have **no charge** — they are **neutral**, like neutrons.

Photon Energies are Usually Given in **Electronvolts**

1) The **energies involved** when you're talking about photons are **so tiny** that it makes sense to use a more
   appropriate unit than the **joule**. Bring on the **electronvolt**...

2) When you **accelerate** an electron between two electrodes,
   it transfers some electrical potential energy (eV) into kinetic energy.

$$eV = \tfrac{1}{2}mv^2$$

   e is the charge on an
   electron: 1.60×10^{-19} C.
   See page 58.

3) An electronvolt is defined as:

   > The **kinetic energy gained** by an **electron** when it is
   > **accelerated** through a **potential difference** of **1 volt**.

4) So 1 electron volt = $e \times V = 1.60 \times 10^{-19}$ C $\times$ 1 JC^{-1}. $\Longrightarrow$ **1 eV = 1.60 × 10^{-19} J**

The **Threshold Voltage** is Used to Find the **Planck Constant**

1) The Planck constant comes up everywhere — but it's not just some random number plucked out of the air.
   You can find its value by doing a simple experiment with **light-emitting diodes** (**LEDs**).

2) Current will only pass through an LED after a **minimum voltage** is placed across it — the **threshold voltage** V_0.

3) This is the voltage needed to give the electrons the **same energy** as a
   photon emitted by the LED. **All** of the electron's **kinetic energy** after it is
   accelerated over this potential difference is **transferred** into a **photon**.

$$E = \frac{hc}{\lambda} = eV_0 \Rightarrow h = \frac{(eV_0)\lambda}{c}$$

4) So by finding the threshold voltage for a particular wavelength LED,
   you can estimate the Planck constant.

Light — Wave or Particle

You can Use LEDs to Estimate the Planck Constant

You've just seen the **theory** of how to find the **Planck constant** — now it's time for the **practicalities**.

Experiment to Measure the Planck Constant

1) Connect an LED of known wavelength in the electrical circuit shown.

2) Start off with no current flowing through the circuit, then adjust the variable resistor until a current just begins to flow through the circuit and the LED lights up.

3) Record the voltage (V_0) across the LED, and the wavelength of light the LED emits.

4) Repeat this experiment with a number of LEDs of different colours that emit light at different wavelengths.

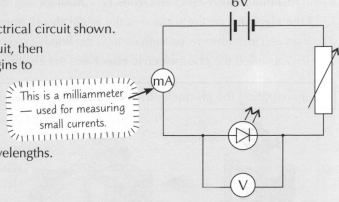

This is a milliammeter — used for measuring small currents.

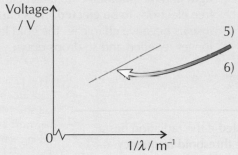

5) Plot a graph of threshold voltages (V_0) against $1/\lambda$ (where λ is the wavelength of light emitted by the LED in metres).

6) You should get a straight line graph with a gradient of hc/e — which you can then use to find the value of h.

E.g. gradient $= \dfrac{hc}{e} = 1.24 \times 10^{-6}$

so $h = \dfrac{1.24 \times 10^{-6}e}{c} = \dfrac{(1.24 \times 10^{-6}) \times (1.6 \times 10^{-19})}{3 \times 10^8}$

$= 6.6 \times 10^{-34}$ Js (to 2 s.f.)

Practice Questions

Q1 Give two different ways to describe the nature of light.

Q2 What is a photon?

Q3 Write down the two formulas you can use to find the energy of a photon. Include the meanings of all the symbols you use.

Q4 What is an electronvolt? What is 1 eV in joules?

Q5 Describe an experiment to determine the Planck constant using different coloured LEDs.

After careful measurements, Fluffles determined that her plank was indeed constant.

Exam Question

Q1 An LED is tested and found to have a threshold voltage of 1.70 V.

a) Calculate the energy of the photons emitted by the LED. Give your answer in joules. [2 marks]

b) The LED emits light with a wavelength of 700 nm, given to 3 significant figures. Use your answer from a) to calculate an estimate for the value of the Planck constant. [2 marks]

Millions of light particles are hitting your retinas as you read this... PANIC...

I hate it in physics when they tell you lies, make you learn it, and just when you've got to grips with it they tell you it was all a load of codswallop. It just makes me doubt all the other things they say. I bet the Earth isn't even round.
*Adjusts tin foil hat.* Ahem. This actually is the real deal folks — light isn't just the nice wave you've always known...

The Photoelectric Effect

The photoelectric effect was one of the original troublemakers in the light-is-it-a-wave-or-a-particle problem...

Shining Light on a Metal can Release Electrons

If you shine **electromagnetic waves** (e.g. light) of a **high enough frequency** onto the **surface of a metal**, it will **instantaneously eject electrons**. For **most** metals, this **frequency** falls in the **U.V.** range.

1) **Free electrons** on the **surface** of the metal **absorb energy** from the light.

2) If an electron absorbs **enough** energy, the **bonds** holding it to the metal **break** and it is **emitted from the surface**.

3) This is called the **photoelectric effect** and the electrons emitted are called **photoelectrons**.

Demonstrating the photoelectric effect with a gold-leaf electroscope

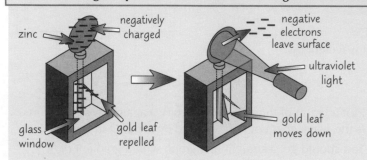

1) The electroscope plate is initially **negatively** charged, so the gold leaf is **repelled**.

2) The zinc plate is then exposed to **ultraviolet light** and the photoelectric effect causes its free electrons to be **ejected**. This causes it to lose its negative charge — the gold leaf is no longer repelled and so drops down.

These are the two that had scientists puzzled. They can't be explained using wave theory.

Conclusion 1: For a given metal, **no photoelectrons are emitted** if the radiation has a frequency **below** a certain value — called the **threshold frequency**.

Conclusion 2: The photoelectrons are emitted with a variety of kinetic energies ranging from zero to some maximum value. This value of **maximum kinetic energy** increases with the **frequency** of the radiation, and is **unaffected** by the **intensity** of the radiation.

Conclusion 3: The **number** of photoelectrons emitted per second is **proportional** to the **intensity** of the radiation.

The Photoelectric Effect Couldn't be Explained by Wave Theory

According to wave theory:

1) For a particular frequency of light, the **energy** carried is **proportional** to the **intensity** of the beam.

2) The energy carried by the light would be **spread evenly** over the wavefront.

3) **Each** free electron on the surface of the metal would gain a **bit of energy** from each incoming wave.

4) Gradually, each electron would gain **enough energy** to leave the metal.

SO... The **higher the intensity** of the wave, the **more energy** it should transfer to each electron — the kinetic energy should increase with **intensity**. There's **no explanation** for the **kinetic energy** depending only on the **frequency**.

There is also **no explanation** for the **threshold frequency**. According to **wave theory**, the electrons should be emitted **eventually**, no matter what the **frequency** is.

The Photon Model Explained the Photoelectric Effect Nicely

According to the photon model (see page 92):

1) When light hits its surface, the metal is **bombarded** by photons.

2) If one of these photons is **absorbed** by a free electron, the electron will gain energy equal to *hf*.

Before an electron can **leave** the surface of the metal, it needs enough energy to **break the bonds holding it there**. This energy is called the **work function energy** (symbol ϕ, phi) and its **value** depends on the **metal**.

The Photoelectric Effect

The *Photon Model* Explains the *Threshold Frequency*...

1) If the energy **gained** by an electron (on the surface of the metal) from a photon is **greater** than the **work function**, the electron is **emitted**.

2) If it **isn't**, the metal will heat up, but **no electrons** will be emitted.

3) Since, for **electrons** to be released, $hf \geq \phi$, the **threshold frequency** must be:

$$f = \frac{\phi}{h}$$

... and the *Maximum Kinetic Energy*

1) The **energy transferred** to an electron is hf.

2) The **kinetic energy** it will be carrying when it **leaves** the metal will be hf **minus** any energy it's **lost** on the way out (there are loads of ways it can do that, and so the emitted electrons have a **range** of energies).

3) The **minimum** amount of energy an electron can lose is the **work function energy**, so the **maximum kinetic energy** is given by **Einstein's photoelectric equation**:

$$hf = \phi + KE_{max} \quad \text{where} \quad KE_{max} = \frac{1}{2}mv_{max}^2$$

$hf = \phi + KE_{max}$ can be rearranged to $KE_{max} = hf - \phi$. This is the same format as $y = mx + c$, so if you plot a graph of KE_{max} against f, the gradient of the line will be h.

4) The **kinetic energy** of the electrons is **independent of the intensity** of the radiation, because they can **only absorb one photon** at a time. A **higher intensity** just means **more** photons hitting a given area per second.

5) But, the **rate of photoelectron emission** is **directly proportional** to the **intensity** of radiation provided it's above the **threshold frequency** — more photons per second means more collisions.

Practice Questions

Q1 Describe an experiment that demonstrates the photoelectric effect.
Q2 What is meant by the term threshold frequency?
Q3 Write down the equation that relates the work function of a metal and the threshold frequency.
Q4 Write down an equation that relates the maximum kinetic energy of a photoelectron released from a metal surface and the frequency of the incident light on the surface.

Exam Questions

$h = 6.63 \times 10^{-34}$ Js; $e = 1.60 \times 10^{-19}$ C

Q1 The work function of calcium is 2.9 eV. Calculate the threshold frequency of radiation needed for the photoelectric effect to take place. [2 marks]

Q2 The surface of a copper plate is illuminated with monochromatic ultraviolet light, with a frequency of 2.0×10^{15} Hz. The work function for copper is 4.7 eV.

a) Calculate the energy in eV carried by one photon of the ultraviolet light. [2 marks]

b) Calculate the maximum kinetic energy of a photoelectron emitted from the copper surface. [2 marks]

Q3 Explain why the photoelectric effect only occurs after the incident light has reached a certain frequency. [2 marks]

I'm so glad we got that all cleared up...

Yep, the photoelectric effect is a bit tricky. The most important bits here are why wave theory doesn't explain the phenomenon, and why the photon theory does. A good way to learn conceptual stuff like this is to try to explain it to someone else. You'll get most formulas in your handy data sheet, but it's probably a good idea to learn them too...

Wave-Particle Duality

Is it a wave? Is it a particle? No, it's a wave. No, it's a particle. No it's not, it's a wave. No don't be daft, it's a particle. (etc.)

Interference and Diffraction show Light as a Wave

1) Light produces **interference** and **diffraction** patterns — **alternating bands** of **dark** and **light**.
2) These can **only** be explained using **waves interfering constructively** (when two waves overlap in phase) or **interfering destructively** (when the two waves are out of phase). (See p.84.)

The Photoelectric Effect Shows Light Behaving as a Particle

1) **Einstein** explained the results of **photoelectricity experiments** (see p.94) by thinking of the **beam of light** as a series of **particle-like photons**.
2) If a **photon** of light is a **discrete** bundle of energy, then it can **interact** with an **electron** in a **one-to-one way**.
3) **All** the **energy** in the **photon** is **given** to one **electron**.

De Broglie Came up With the Wave-Particle Duality Theory

1) Louis de Broglie made a **bold suggestion** in his **PhD thesis**:

> If **'wave-like'** light showed **particle properties** (photons), **'particles'** like **electrons** should be expected to show **wave-like properties**.

2) The **de Broglie equation** relates a **wave property** (**wavelength**, λ) to a **moving particle property** (momentum, p). h = Planck constant = 6.63×10^{-34} Js.

I'm not impressed — this is just speculation. What do you think Dad?

$$\lambda = \frac{h}{p}$$

3) The de Broglie wave of a particle can be interpreted as a **'probability wave'** — the **likelihood** of finding a particle at a point is **directly proportional** to the **square** of the **amplitude** of the wave at that point.
4) Many physicists at the time **weren't very impressed** — his ideas were just **speculation**. But later experiments **confirmed** the wave nature of electrons.

Electron Diffraction shows the Wave Nature of Electrons

1) In **1927**, two American physicists, **Clinton Davisson** and **Lester Germer**, succeeded in diffracting **electrons**.
2) **Diffraction patterns** are observed when **accelerated electrons** in a vacuum tube **interact** with the **spaces** between **carbon atoms** in **polycrystalline graphite**.
3) This **confirms** that electrons show **wave-like** properties.
4) According to wave theory, the **spread** of the **lines** in the diffraction pattern **increases** if the **wavelength** of the wave is **greater**.
5) In electron diffraction experiments, a **smaller accelerating voltage**, i.e. **slower** electrons, gives **widely spaced** rings.
6) **Increase** the **electron speed** and the diffraction pattern circles **squash together** towards the **middle**. This fits in with the **de Broglie** equation above — if the **momentum** is **higher**, the **wavelength** is **shorter** and the **spread** of lines is **smaller**.
7) Electron diffraction was a **huge** discovery — this was the first **direct evidence** for de Broglie's theory.

> In general, λ for **electrons** accelerated in a **vacuum tube** is about the **same** size as **electromagnetic waves** in the **X-ray** part of the spectrum.

Wave-Particle Duality

Particles Don't show Wave-Like Properties All the Time

1) You **only** get **diffraction** if a particle interacts with an object of about the **same size** as its **de Broglie wavelength**.

2) A **tennis ball**, for example, with **mass 0.058 kg** and **speed 100 ms⁻¹** has a **de Broglie wavelength** of **10⁻³⁴ m**. That's **10¹⁹ times smaller** than the **nucleus** of an **atom**! There's nothing that small for it to interact with.

> **Example:** An electron of mass 9.11×10^{-31} kg is fired from an electron gun at 7.00×10^6 ms⁻¹. What size object will the electron need to interact with in order to diffract?
>
> Momentum of electron $= p = mv = (9.11 \times 10^{-31}) \times (7.00 \times 10^6) = 6.377 \times 10^{-24}$ kg ms⁻¹
>
> $\lambda = \dfrac{h}{p} = \dfrac{6.63 \times 10^{-34}}{6.377 \times 10^{-24}} = \mathbf{1.04 \times 10^{-10}}$ **m (to 3 s.f.)**

> Electrons with a wavelength of around 1×10^{-10} **m** are **likely** to be diffracted by the atoms in **polycrystalline structures**.

3) A **shorter wavelength** gives **less diffraction effects**. This fact is used in the **electron microscope**.

4) **Diffraction** effects **blur detail** on an image. If you want to **resolve tiny detail** in an **image**, you need a **shorter wavelength**. **Light** blurs out detail more than 'electron-waves' do, so an **electron microscope** can resolve **finer detail** than a **light microscope**. They can let you look at things as tiny as a single strand of DNA... which is nice.

Practice Questions

Q1 Which observations show light to have a 'wave-like' character?

Q2 Which observations show light to have a 'particle' character?

Q3 What happens to the de Broglie wavelength of a particle if its velocity increases?

Q4 Describe the experimental evidence that shows electrons have a 'wave-like' character.

Exam Questions

proton mass, $m_p = 1.673 \times 10^{-27}$ kg; electron mass, $m_e = 9.11 \times 10^{-31}$ kg

Q1 a) State what is meant by the wave-particle duality of electromagnetic radiation. [1 mark]

   b) Calculate the momentum of an electron with a de Broglie wavelength of 590 nm. [2 marks]

Q2 Electrons travelling at a speed of 3.50×10^6 ms⁻¹ exhibit wave properties.

   a) Calculate the wavelength of these electrons. [2 marks]

   b) Calculate the speed of protons which would have the same wavelength as these electrons. [2 marks]

   c) Some electrons and protons were accelerated from rest by the same potential difference, giving them the same kinetic energy. Explain why they will have different wavelengths. [3 marks]

Q3 Electrons are directed at a thin slice of graphite at high speed and a diffraction pattern is observed. Which of the following statements correctly describe a conclusion that this observation supports? [1 mark]

   1 Electrons can show particle-like behaviour.
   2 Waves can show particle-like behaviour.
   3 Photons can show wave-like behaviour.
   4 Electrons can show wave-like behaviour.

   A 1, 2 and 4   B 4 only   C 3 only   D 1 and 4 only

Don't hide your wave-particles under a bushel...

Right — I think we'll all agree that quantum physics is a wee bit strange when you come to think about it. What it's saying is that electrons and photons aren't really waves, and they aren't really particles — they're both... at the same time. It's what quantum physicists like to call a 'juxtaposition of states'. Well they would, wouldn't they...

Answers

Module 1 — Development of Practical Skills in Physics

Page 5 — Planning and Implementing

1 a) Independent variable: light level / distance from the light source, dependent variable: resistance of the LDR *[1 mark]*.

  b) Any two of: e.g. the light source used / the background lighting in the room / the temperature of the room/LDR/wires / the potential difference / the power supply the LDR is connected to / the length of wires in the circuit / the type of wires in the circuit / the multimeter used to measure the resistance.
  [2 marks available — 1 mark for each correct answer.]

Page 7 — Analysing Results

1 a)

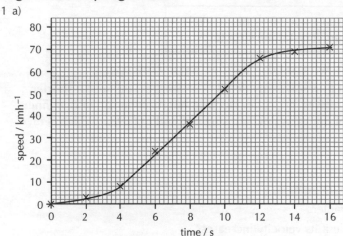

  [1 mark for both axes drawn to a sensible scale and 1 mark for labelling both axes correctly, 1 mark for all the points drawn correctly, and 1 mark for a sensible line of best fit.]

  b) The graph is linear between 4 and 10 seconds *[1 mark]*.
  Accept 11 seconds as the upper limit if the graph in part a) agrees.

  c) The maximum acceleration is the value of the steepest gradient, which is the linear portion of the graph *[1 mark]*:

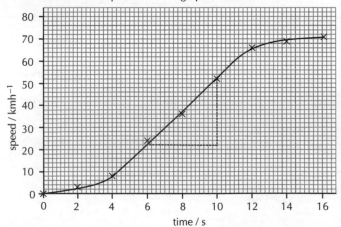

  change in speed = $52 - 22 = 30$ km hr^{-1} = $30 \div (60 \times 60)$
  $\qquad\qquad\qquad = 0.008333...$ km s^{-1} *[1 mark]*
  change in time = $10 - 6 = 4$ s *[1 mark]*
  acceleration = $0.008333... \div 4 = 0.002083...$ km s^{-2}
  $\qquad\qquad = \mathbf{0.0021}$ **km s^{-2}** or **27000 km hr^{-2} (to 2 s.f.)** *[1 mark]*
  Accept an answer in the range 0.0020-0.0022 km s^{-2} or 26000-28000 km hr^{-2}.

Page 9 — Evaluating and Concluding

1 $50 - (50 \times 0.02 / 100) = 49.99$ Ω, so the answer is **B**. *[1 mark]*
2 a) $t = 0.32$ seconds, $v = 2.0$ ms^{-1} *[1 mark]*

  b) E.g. The results do not support this conclusion *[1 mark]*, because the student has only collected data for a small range of times so he cannot draw conclusions about times longer than those he measured *[1 mark]* / because the student has only investigated one object so he cannot draw conclusions about other objects *[1 mark]*.

Module 2 — Foundations of Physics

Page 11 — Quantities and Units

1 a) S.I. unit of mass = kg. S.I. unit of volume = m^3.
  $\rho = m / V$ and volume is length cubed, so in S.I. base units
  $\rho = $ kg / m^3 = **kg m^{-3}** *[1 mark]*

  b) $m = 9.8$ g = 9.8×10^{-3} kg
  $V = (11$ mm$)^3 = (11 \times 10^{-3}$ m$)^3 = 1.331 \times 10^{-6}$ m^3 *[1 mark]*
  $\rho = m / V = (9.8 \times 10^{-3}) \div (1.331 \times 10^{-6})$
  $\qquad = 7362.88... = $ **7400 kg m^{-3} (to 2 s.f.)** *[1 mark]*
  You could also have worked this out in g mm^{-3} then converted your answer, but this way is much easier.

Page 13 — Measurements and Uncertainties

1 a) $(0.02 \div 0.52) \times 100 = 3.846... = $ **3.8 % (to 2 s.f.)** *[1 mark]*

  b) $(0.02 \div 0.94) \times 100 = 2.127... = $ **2.1% (to 2 s.f.)** *[1 mark]*

  c) acceleration = change in velocity / time = $(0.94 - 0.52) \div 2.5$
  $\qquad\qquad = 0.168$ ms^{-2} *[1 mark]*
  Absolute error in change of velocity = $0.02 + 0.02 = 0.04$ ms^{-1}
  Percentage error in change of velocity: $(0.04 \div (0.94 - 0.52)) \times 100 = 9.523...\%$
  [1 mark]
  Percentage error in time taken = $(0.5 \div 2.5) \times 100 = 20\%$
  Percentage error in acceleration = $9.523...\% + 20\%$
  $\qquad\qquad\qquad = 29.523...\%$ *[1 mark]*
  Absolute error in acceleration = $0.168 \times (29.523... \div 100)$
  $\qquad\qquad\qquad = 0.0496$ ms^{-2}
  So the acceleration = **0.17 ± 0.05 ms^{-2} (to 2 s.f.)** *[1 mark]*

Answers

Page 15 — Scalars and Vectors

1

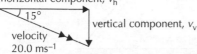

Weight 75 N | θ | Resultant force, F

Wind 20 N

$F^2 = 20^2 + 75^2 = 6025$
So $F = 78$ N (to 2 s.f.)
$\tan \theta = 20 / 75 = 0.266...$
So $\theta = \tan^{-1} 0.266... = 15°$ (to 2 s.f.)
The resultant force on the rock is **78 N (to 2 s.f.) [1 mark]**
at an angle of **15° (to 2 s.f.) [1 mark]** to the vertical.
Make sure you know which angle you're finding — and label it on your diagram.

2   horizontal component, v_h

15°

vertical component, v_v

velocity 20.0 ms⁻¹

horizontal component $v_h = 20.0 \times \cos 15.0°$
       $= \textbf{19.3 ms}^{-1}$ **(to 3 s.f.) [1 mark]**
vertical component $v_v = 20 \times \sin 15.0°$
       $= \textbf{5.18 ms}^{-1}$ **(to 3 s.f.) [1 mark]**

3   E.g.
current, $v_{river} = 0.20$ ms⁻¹ v_h

120°   60°

driving velocity, $v_{boat} = 1.54$ ms⁻¹

R

v_v

horizontal component $v_{river} = 0.20$ ms⁻¹
vertical component $v_{river} = 0$ ms⁻¹
horizontal component $v_{boat} = 1.54 \times \cos 60 = 0.77$ ms⁻¹
vertical component $v_{boat} = 1.54 \times \sin 60 = 1.333...$ ms⁻¹
So, horizontal $v_{resultant} = 0.20 + 0.77 = 0.97$ ms⁻¹ *[1 mark]*
vertical $v_{resultant} = 0 + 1.333... = 1.333...$ ms⁻¹ *[1 mark]*
Combine the vertical and horizontal components of R.

$v_h = 0.97$ ms⁻¹

θ

R

$v_v = 1.333...$ ms⁻¹

$v_{resultant} = \sqrt{0.97^2 + 1.333...^2} = 1.649...$ ms⁻¹
       $= \textbf{1.6 ms}^{-1}$ **(to 2 s.f) [1 mark]**

$\tan \theta = 1.333... \div 0.97 = \tan^{-1} 1.374...$ so $\theta = \textbf{54°}$ **(to 2 s.f)**
So the resultant velocity of the boat is 1.6 ms⁻¹ at an angle of 54°
to the current *[1 mark]*.

Module 3: Section 1 — Motion

Page 17 — Motion with Constant Acceleration

1 a) $a = -9.81$ ms⁻², $t = 5$ s, $u = 0$ ms⁻¹, $v = ?$
    use : $v = u + at$
           $v = 0 + 5 \times -9.81$ *[1 mark]*
           $v = -49.05 = \textbf{-49 ms}^{-1}$ **(to 2 s.f.)** *[1 mark]*.
    NB: It's negative because she's falling downwards and we took upwards as
    the positive direction.

  b) Use: $s = \left(\dfrac{u+v}{2}\right)t$ or $s = ut + \frac{1}{2}at^2$

      $s = \dfrac{-49.05}{2} \times 5$ $s = 0 + \frac{1}{2} \times -9.81 \times 5^2$ *[1 mark]*

      $s = -122.625$ m $s = -122.625$ m
    So she falls **120 m (to 2 s.f.)** *[1 mark]*

2 a) $v = 0$ ms⁻¹, $t = 3.2$ s, $s = 40$ m, $u = ?$
    use: $s = \left(\dfrac{u+v}{2}\right)t$
    $40 = 3.2u \div 2$ *[1 mark]*
    $u = 80 \div 3.2 = \textbf{25 ms}^{-1}$ *[1 mark]*

  b) Use: $v^2 = u^2 + 2as$
    $0 = 25^2 + 80a$ *[1 mark]*
    $-80a = 625$
    $a = -7.81... = \textbf{-7.8 ms}^{-2}$ **(to 2 s.f.)** *[1 mark]*
    You could also have solved this using $v = u + at$.

3 a) Take upstream as negative: $v = 5$ ms⁻¹, $a = 6$ ms⁻², $s = 1.2$ m,
    $u = ?$
    use: $v^2 = u^2 + 2as$
    $5^2 = u^2 + 2 \times 6 \times 1.2$ *[1 mark]*
    $u^2 = 25 - 14.4 = 10.6$
    $u = -3.255... = \textbf{-3.3 ms}^{-1}$ **(to 2 s.f.)** *[1 mark]*
    *The negative root is taken because the boat is pushed upstream at the
    start, which we've taken to be the negative direction.*

  b) From furthest point: $u = 0$ ms⁻¹, $a = 6$ ms⁻², $v = 5$ ms⁻¹, $s = ?$
    use: $v^2 = u^2 + 2as$ *[1 mark]*
    $5^2 = 0 + 2 \times 6 \times s$
    $s = 25 \div 12 = \textbf{2.1 m (to 2 s.f.)}$ *[1 mark]*

4 a) Use $v = u + at$
    In the first second, $u = 3$, $v = 3 + a$
    In the second second, $u = 3 + a$, $v = (3 + a) + a = 3 + 2a$
    In the third second, $u = 3 + 2a$, $v = (3 + 2a) + a = 3 + 3a$
    [1 mark]
    For the third second, use: $s = \left(\dfrac{u+v}{2}\right)t$

    $6 = \left(\dfrac{3 + 2a + 3 + 3a}{2}\right) \times 1 = \left(\dfrac{6 + 5a}{2}\right)$

    $12 = 6 + 5a$

    $6 = 5a$

    $a = \textbf{1.2 ms}^{-1}$ *[1 mark]*

    There's another way to work out acceleration — the cyclist travelled 6 m
    in the third second, so at $t = 2.5$ seconds his speed must have been exactly
    6 ms⁻¹. You can use acceleration = change in speed ÷ time taken and get
    $a = 3 \div 2.5 = 1.2$ ms⁻².

  b) In the fourth second, $u = 3 + 3a$, $v = (3 + 3a) + a = 3 + 4a$
    Use $s = \left(\dfrac{u+v}{2}\right)t$ for the fourth second:
    $s = \frac{1}{2}(3 + 3a + 3 + 4a) \times 1 = \frac{1}{2}(6 + 7 \times 1.2) \times 1$

    $= 3 + 4.2 = \textbf{7.2 m}$ *[1 mark]*

Answers

Page 19 — Free Fall

1 a) The student needs the computer to record:
The time for the first strip of card to pass through the beam *[1 mark]*
The time for the second strip of card to pass through the beam *[1 mark]*
The time between these events *[1 mark]*

b) Average speed of first strip while it breaks the light beam =
width of strip ÷ time to pass through beam *[1 mark]*
Average speed of second strip while it breaks the light beam =
width of strip ÷ time to pass through beam *[1 mark]*
Acceleration = (second speed – first speed)
÷ time between light beam being broken *[1 mark]*

c) E.g. the device will accelerate while the beam is broken by the strips *[1 mark]*.

2 a) You know $s = 5$ m, $a = -g$, $v = 0$
You need to find u, so use $v^2 = u^2 + 2as$
$0 = u^2 - 2 \times 9.81 \times 5$ *[1 mark]*
$u^2 = 98.1$, so $u = 9.90... = $ **9.9 ms⁻¹ (to 2 s.f.)** *[1 mark]*

b) You know $a = -g$, $v = 0$ at highest point, $u = 9.90...$ ms⁻¹
You need to find t, so use $v = u + at$
$0 = 9.90... - 9.81t$ *[1 mark]*
$t = 9.90.../9.81 = $ **1.0 s (to 2 s.f.)** *[1 mark]*

c) Her velocity as she lands back on the trampoline will be
–9.9 ms⁻¹ (to 2 s.f.) (same magnitude, opposite direction)
[1 mark]

Page 21 — Projectile Motion

1 a) You only need to worry about the vertical motion of the stone.
$u = 0$ ms⁻¹, $s = -560$ m, $a = -g = -9.81$ ms⁻², $t = ?$
You need to find t, so use: $s = ut + \frac{1}{2} at^2$
$-560 = 0 + \frac{1}{2} \times -9.81 \times t^2$
$t = \sqrt{\dfrac{2 \times (-560)}{-9.81}}$ *[1 mark]*
$t = 10.68... = $ **11 s (to 2 s.f.)** *[1 mark]*

b) You know that in the horizontal direction:
$v = 20$ m/s, $t = 10.68...$ s, $a = 0$, $s = ?$
$s = v \times t = 20 \times 10.68...$ *[1 mark]*
$s = 213.69... = $ **210 m (to 2 s.f.)** *[1 mark]*

2 C *[1 mark]*
Use $v^2 = u^2 + 2as$ to find the vertical displacement when $v = 0$. The arrow was fired from 1 m above the ground so don't forget to include the extra metre in your calculations.

Page 23 — Displacement-Time Graphs

1 Split graph into four sections:

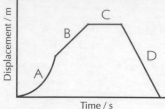

A: acceleration *[1 mark]*
B: constant velocity *[1 mark]*
C: stationary *[1 mark]*
D: constant velocity in opposite direction to A and B *[1 mark]*

2 a)

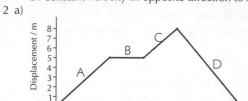

[4 marks — 1 mark for each section correctly drawn]

b) At A: $v = s \div t = 5 \div 8 = 0.625 = $ **0.63 ms⁻¹ (to 2 s.f)**
At B: $v = $ **0 ms⁻¹**
At C: $v = 3 \div 5 = $ **0.6 ms⁻¹**
At D: $v = -8 \div 10 = $ **–0.8 ms⁻¹**
[2 marks for all correct or just 1 mark for 2 or 3 correct]

Answers

Page 25 — Velocity-Time Graphs

1 a)

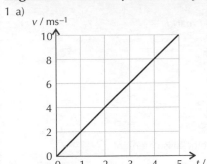

[1 mark for correct axes, 1 mark for correct line]

b) Use $s = ut + \frac{1}{2}at^2$
$t = 1$, $s = $ **1 m**
$t = 2$, $s = $ **4 m**
$t = 3$, $s = $ **9 m**
$t = 4$, $s = $ **16 m**
$t = 5$, $s = $ **25 m**
[2 marks for all correct or 1 mark for at least 3 pairs of values right]

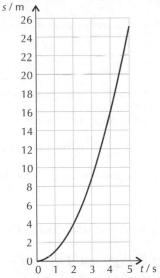

[1 mark for correctly labelled axes, 1 mark for correct curve]

c) E.g. another way to calculate displacement is to find the area under the velocity-time graph *[1 mark]*.
E.g. total displacement = $\frac{1}{2} \times 5 \times 10 = $ **25 m** *[1 mark]*

Page 27 — Motion Experiments and Stopping Distances

1 a) Reaction time is 0.5 s, speed is 20 ms^{-1}
$s = vt = 20 \times 0.5$ *[1 mark]* = **10 m** *[1 mark]*

b) Use $F = ma$ to get a: $a = -10\,000/850 = -11.76...$ *[1 mark]*
Use $v^2 = u^2 + 2as$, and rearrange
$s = (0^2 - 20^2) \div (2 \times -11.76...)$ *[1 mark]*
= **17 m** *[1 mark]*
Remember that a force against the direction of motion is negative.

c) No. Total stopping distance = 10 + 17 = 27 m
She stops 3 m before the cow. *[1 mark]*

2 a) Using a rougher ramp material would create more friction *[1 mark]*, which would cause more drag on the toy car and decrease its velocity *[1 mark]*.

b) E.g. The starting position of the car *[1 mark]*. The higher the car started up the ramp, the more time it would have to accelerate, so the greater its velocity would be *[1 mark]*. /
Using similar sized but different shaped cars *[1 mark]*. The cars which were more streamlined would achieve a higher velocity as they are less affected by air resistance *[1 mark]*.

Module 3: Section 2 — Forces in Action

Page 29 — Forces and Acceleration

1 a)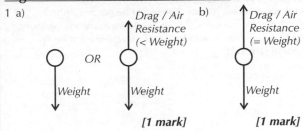

[1 mark]   *[1 mark]*

The relative sizes of the arrows in a force diagram tell you the relative magnitude of the forces.

2 a) Net force = 500 − 100 − 300 = **100 N** *[1 mark]*
b) $a = F \div m$ (from $F = ma$)
= $100 \div 250 = $ **0.4 ms^{-2}** *[1 mark]*

Page 31 — Forces and Equilibrium

1

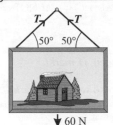

Weight = vertical component of tension × 2
$60 = 2T \sin 50°$ *[1 mark]*
$60 = 2T \times 0.766...$
$78.3... = 2T$
$T = 39.1... = $ **39 N (to 2 s.f.)** *[1 mark]*

2

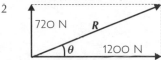

By Pythagoras:
$R = \sqrt{1200^2 + 720^2} = 1399.42... = $ **1400 N (to 3 s.f.)** *[1 mark]*
$\tan \theta = \frac{720}{1200}$, so $\theta = \tan^{-1} 0.6 = 30.96... = 31.0°$ (to 3 s.f.)
So the direction of the resultant force is **31.0° (to 3 s.f.) from the horizontal** *[1 mark]*

Page 33 — Mass, Weight and Centre of Mass

1 B *[1 mark]*
On Earth, $W = mg$, so $m = W/g = X/g$.

2 a) Hang the object freely from a point so that it hangs vertically. Hang a plumb bob from the same point, and use it to draw a vertical line down the object *[1 mark]*. Repeat for a different point and find the point of intersection *[1 mark]*.
The centre of gravity is halfway through the thickness of the object (by symmetry) at the point of intersection *[1 mark]*.

b) E.g. Source: the object and/or plumb line might move slightly while you're drawing the vertical line *[1 mark]*.
Reduced by: hang the object from a third point to confirm the position of the point of intersection *[1 mark]*.

Answers

Page 36 — Drag and Terminal Velocity

1 a) The velocity increases at a steady rate, which means the acceleration is constant *[1 mark]*.
Constant acceleration means there must be no atmospheric resistance (atmospheric resistance would increase with velocity, leading to a decrease in acceleration). So there must be no atmosphere *[1 mark]*.

b) velocity

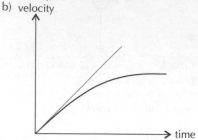

[1 mark for a smooth curve that levels out, 1 mark for correct position relative to existing line]
Your graph must be a smooth curve which levels out. It must NOT go down at the end.

c) (The graph becomes less steep)
because the acceleration is decreasing *[1 mark]*
because air resistance increases with speed *[1 mark]*
(The graph levels out)
because air resistance has become equal to weight *[1 mark]*
If the question says 'explain', you won't get marks for just describing what the graph shows — you have to say why it is that shape.

2 a) The 15 cm cone will have the lowest terminal velocity *[1 mark]* because it has the largest surface area and therefore the largest drag *[1 mark]*.

b) velocity

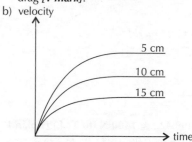

[3 marks, 1 mark for each correct line.]

c) E.g. The shape/slant/height of the cone because it would affect the amount of air resistance *[1 mark]*.

d) The curve for the largest cone would reach a higher terminal velocity *[1 mark]* because the shape is more streamlined *[1 mark]* so the air resistance would be lower at a given speed *[1 mark]*.

Page 37 — Density, Pressure and Upthrust

1 a) $\rho = \frac{m}{V}$
V of cylinder $= \pi r^2 h = \pi \times 4^2 \times 6 = 301.59...$ cm^{-3} *[1 mark]*
$\rho = 820 \div 301.59... = 2.71... = $ **2.7 g cm^{-3} (to 2 s.f.)** *[1 mark]*

b) $V = 5 \times 5 \times 5 = 125$ cm^3
$m = \rho \times V = 2.71... \times 125 = 339.86... = $ **340 g (to 2 s.f.)** *[1 mark]*

2 $A = 1.72 \times 1.72 = 2.9584$ m^2 *[1 mark]*
$p = \frac{F}{A} = \frac{17}{2.9584} = 5.746... = $ **5.75 Pa (to 3 s.f.)** *[1 mark]*

3 $p = h\rho g = 2.4 \times 1024 \times 9.81 = 24109.056$
$= $ **24000 Pa (to 2 s.f.)** *[1 mark]*

4 Upthrust = weight of fluid displaced.
Volume of water displaced $= \frac{4}{3}\pi r^3 = \frac{4}{3}\pi \times (0.052)^3$
$= 5.889... \times 10^{-4}$ m *[1 mark]*
$\rho = \frac{m}{V}$, so mass of water displaced $= \rho V$
$= 1050 \times 5.889... \times 10^{-4}$
$= 0.6184...$ kg *[1 mark]*
$W = mg = 0.6184... \times 9.81 = 6.066...$
$= $ **6.07 N (to 3 s.f.)** *[1 mark]*

Page 39— Moments and Torques

1 torque = force × distance
$60 = 0.4F$, so $F = $ **150 N** *[1 mark]*

2

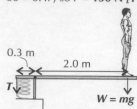

0.3 m   2.0 m
T $W = mg$

clockwise moment = anticlockwise moment
$W \times 2.0 = T \times 0.3$
$60 \times 9.81 \times 2.0 = T \times 0.3$ *[1 mark]*
$T = $ **3900 N (to 2 s.f.)** *[1 mark]*
The tension in the spring is equal and opposite to the force exerted by the diver on the spring.

Module 3: Section 3 — Work, Energy and Power

Page 41 — Work and Power

1) a)

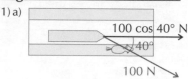

100 cos 40° N
40°
100 N

Force in direction of travel = 100 cos40° = 76.6... N *[1 mark]*
$W = Fx = 76.6... \times 1500 = 114906...$
$= $ **110 000 J (to 2 s.f.)** *[1 mark]*

b) Use $P = Fv$
$= 100 \cos40° \times 0.8$ *[1 mark]* $= 61.2... = $ **61 W (to 2 s.f.)** *[1 mark]*

2) a) Use $W = Fx$
$= 20 \times 9.81 \times 3$ *[1 mark]* $= 588.6 = $ **590 J (to 2 s.f.)** *[1 mark]*
Remember that 20 kg is not the force — it's the mass. So you need to multiply it by 9.81 Nkg^{-1} to get the weight.

b) Use $P = Fv$
$= 20 \times 9.81 \times 0.25$ *[1 mark]* $= 49.05 = $ **49 W (to 2 s.f.)** *[1 mark]*

Page 43 — Conservation of Energy and Efficiency

1 a) Use $E_k = \frac{1}{2}mv^2$ and $E_p = mgh$ *[1 mark]*
$\frac{1}{2}mv^2 = mgh$
$\frac{1}{2}v^2 = gh$
$v^2 = 2gh = 2 \times 9.81 \times 2 = 39.24$ *[1 mark]*
$v = \sqrt{39.24} = $ **6.3 ms^{-1} (to 2 s.f.)** *[1 mark]*
'No friction' allows you to say that the changes in kinetic and potential energy will be the same.

b) 2 m — no friction means the kinetic energy will all change back into potential energy, so he will rise back up to the same height as he started *[1 mark]*.

c) Put in some more energy by actively 'skating' / 'pumping the board' *[1 mark]*.

2 a) If there's no air resistance, $E_k = E_p = mgh$ *[1 mark]*
$E_k = 0.02 \times 9.81 \times 8 = 1.5696 = $ **1.6 J (to 2 s.f.)** *[1 mark]*

b) If the ball rebounds to 6.5 m, it has gravitational potential energy:
$E_p = mgh = 0.02 \times 9.81 \times 6.5 = 1.2753$ *[1 mark]*
So $1.5696 - 1.2753 = 0.2943 = $ **0.29 J (to 2 s.f.)** is converted to other forms *[1 mark]*.

You could also work out the loss of E_p from the difference in height —
$E_p = 0.02 \times 9.81 \times (8 - 6.5) = 0.29$ J (to 2 s.f.).

3 Use efficiency $= \frac{\text{useful output energy}}{\text{total input energy}} \times 100$
$= (140 - 65) \div 140 \times 100 = 53.5... = $ **54% (to 2 s.f.)** *[1 mark]*

Answers

Module 3: Section 4 — Materials

Page 45 — Hooke's Law

1 a) Force is proportional to extension. The force is 1.5 times as great, so the new extension will also be 1.5 times the original extension. new extension = 1.5 × 4.0 mm = **6.0 mm** ***[1 mark]***

b) $F = kx$ and so $k = F/x$
$k = 10 \div (4.0 \times 10^{-3})$ = **2500 Nm^{-1}** ***[1 mark]***

c) Any one from e.g. the string now stretches much further for small increases in force ***[1 mark]***. / When the string is loosened it is longer than at the start ***[1 mark]***.

2 The rubber band does not obey Hooke's law ***[1 mark]*** because when the force is doubled from 2.5 N to 5.0 N, the extension increases by a factor of 2.3. ***[1 mark]***.
Or you could show that k is different for 2.5 N and 5.0 N.

Page 47 — Stress, Strain and Elastic Potential Energy

1 a) $\varepsilon = x/l = 4.0 \times 10^{-3}/2.00$ = **2.0×10^{-3} (to 2 s.f.)** ***[1 mark]***

b) $\sigma = F/A$
$A = \pi r^2$ or $\pi(d^2/4) = \pi \times ((1.0 \times 10^{-3})^2 \div 4)$
$= 7.8539... \times 10^{-7}$ m^2 ***[1 mark]***
$\sigma = F/A = 300/(7.8539... \times 10^{-7})$
= **3.8×10^8 Nm^{-2} (to 2 s.f.)** ***[1 mark]***

2 a) $F = kx$ so $k = F/x = 50/(3.0 \times 10^{-3})$
= **1.7×10^4 Nm^{-1} (to 2 s.f.)** ***[1 mark]***

b) $E = \frac{1}{2}Fx = \frac{1}{2} \times 50 \times 3.0 \times 10^{-3}$ = **7.5×10^{-2} J** ***[1 mark]***

3 $E = \frac{1}{2}kx^2 = \frac{1}{2} \times 40.8 \times 0.05^2 = 0.051$ J ***[1 mark]***
To find maximum speed, assume all this energy is converted to kinetic energy in the ball. $E_{kinetic} = E$
$E = \frac{1}{2}mv^2$, so $v^2 = 2E/m$ ***[1 mark]***
$v^2 = (2 \times 0.051)/0.012 = 8.5$, so v = **2.92 ms^{-1} (to 3 s.f.)** ***[1 mark]***

Page 49 — The Young Modulus

1 a) Cross-sectional area = πr^2 or $\pi(d^2/4)$.
So the cross-sectional area = $\pi \times ((0.6 \times 10^{-3})^2 \div 4)$
$= 2.827.... \times 10^{-7}$ = **2.8×10^{-7} m^2 (to 2 s.f.)** ***[1 mark]***

b) $\sigma = F/A = 80/(2.827... \times 10^{-7}) = 2.829... \times 10^8$
= **2.8×10^8 Nm^{-2} (to 2 s.f.)** ***[1 mark]***

c) $\varepsilon = x/l = 3.6 \times 10^{-3}/2.50$ = **1.44×10^{-3}** ***[1 mark]***

d) $E = \sigma/\varepsilon = 2.829... \times 10^8 / (1.44 \times 10^{-3})$ ***[1 mark]*** $= 1.964... \times 10^{11}$
= **2.0×10^{11} Nm^{-2} (to 2 s.f.)** ***[1 mark]***

2 a) $E = \sigma/\varepsilon$ so $\varepsilon = \sigma/E = 2.6 \times 10^8/1.3 \times 10^{11}$ ***[1 mark]***
= **2.0×10^{-3}** ***[1 mark]***

b) $\sigma = F/A$ so $A = F/\sigma = 100/(2.6 \times 10^8)$ = **3.8×10^{-7} m^2 (to 2 s.f.)** ***[1 mark]***

c) Elastic potential energy per unit volume = $\frac{1}{2} \times \sigma \times \varepsilon$
$= \frac{1}{2} \times 2.6 \times 10^8 \times 2.0 \times 10^{-3}$ = **2.6×10^5 Jm^{-3}** ***[1 mark]***

Page 51 — Interpreting Stress-Strain Graphs

1 a) E.g.

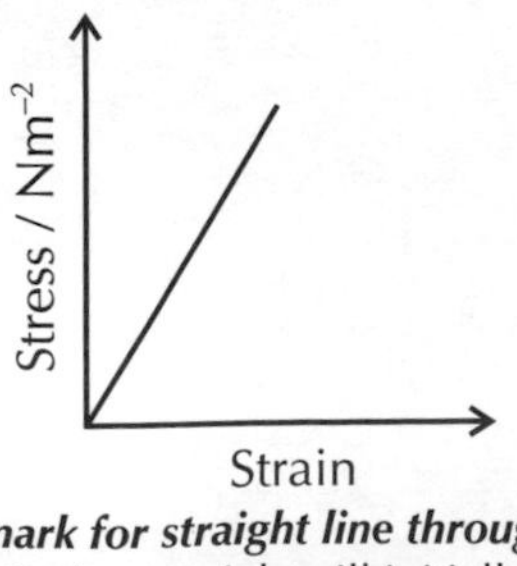

[1 mark for straight line through the origin.]

b) E.g. Both materials will initially obey Hooke's law. After a certain point, the hardened steel will snap ***[1 mark]***, whereas the stress-strain graph for copper will begin to curve / copper will start to show large deformations for small increases in load / copper will begin to deform plastically ***[1 mark]***.

2 a) A ***[1 mark]***

b) B ***[1 mark]***

Module 3: Section 5 — Newton's Laws of Motion and Momentum

Page 53 — Momentum and Impulse

1 a) total momentum before collision = total momentum after
$(0.145 \times 1.94) + 0 = (0.145 \times -0.005) + 0.148v$ ***[1 mark]***
$0.2813 + 0.000725 = 0.148v$, so $v = 1.90557...$
= **1.9 ms^{-1} (to 2 s.f.)** ***[1 mark]***

b) Kinetic energy before the collision =
$(\frac{1}{2} \times 0.145 \times 1.94^2) + (\frac{1}{2} \times 0.148 \times 0^2) = 0.272861$ J
Kinetic energy after the collision =
$(\frac{1}{2} \times 0.145 \times 0.005^2) + (\frac{1}{2} \times 0.148 \times 1.90557...^2) = 0.26871...$ J ***[1 mark]***
The collision is not perfectly elastic / is inelastic ***[1 mark]***, as the kinetic energy is greater before the collision than after it ***[1 mark]***.

c) $F\Delta t = \Delta p = (0.145 \times 0.005) - (0.145 \times 0) = 0.000725$
so $F = \Delta p \div \Delta t$
$= 0.000725 \div 0.15$ ***[1 mark]***
$= 0.00483...$ = **4.8×10^{-3} N (to 2 s.f.)** ***[1 mark]***

Page 55 — Newton's Laws of Motion

1 a) When the parachutist first jumps out of the plane, the only vertical force acting on her is due to gravity, so there is a net downward force ***[1 mark]***. Newton's 2nd law states that, for a body of constant mass, the acceleration is proportional to the net force, so she will accelerate downwards ***[1 mark]***.

b) $F = ma = mg = 78 \times 9.81$ = **765 N (to 3 s.f.)** ***[1 mark]***

c) Newton's 1st law states that a net force is needed to change the velocity of an object — the parachutist's velocity is not changing, so the net force acting on her must be zero ***[1 mark]***.

2 $F = \Delta p / \Delta t$, where $F = 2143 - 213 = 1930$, $\Delta t = 15$
and $\Delta p = m\Delta v = m \times (26.3 - 5.5) = 20.8m$
So $1930 = 20.8m \div 15$
$m = (1930 \times 15) \div 20.8$ ***[1 mark]*** $= 1391.82...$ ***[1 mark]***
So the combined mass of the passengers is
$1391.82... - 1244 = 147.82...$ = **148 kg (to 3 s.f.)** ***[1 mark]***

Answers

Page 57 — Car Safety

1 **5-6 marks:**
The answer clearly explains more than one way that air bags protect passengers, with reference to Newton's second law of motion to explain the forces involved where appropriate. The answer clearly explains the risks associated with air bags when used incorrectly, and suggests how to reduce the risks.
The answer is structured in a logical way, with relevant information supporting it throughout.

3-4 marks:
The answer describes ways in which air bags protect passengers, and explains them with reference to forces involved. The explanation is partly incomplete. The answer gives the risks associated with air bags when used incorrectly, and includes some explanation of these risks or ways to reduce the risks.
The answer has some logical structure, with mostly relevant information supporting it.

1-2 marks:
The answer includes some description of how air bags protect passengers, but no relevant explanation involving forces. The answer has some limited description of the risks associated with air bags when used incorrectly.
The answer is basic, poorly structured and unsupported by relevant information.

0 marks:
No relevant information is given.

Here are some points your answer may include:
- Air bags protect passengers by stopping them from hitting the dashboard/steering wheel/hard surfaces inside the car in a crash.
- Air bags increase the time taken for passengers to come to a complete stop.
- Newton's 2nd Law, $F = \Delta p \div \Delta t$, so by increasing the time that passengers take to come to a stop, air bags reduce the forces acting on passengers in a crash (for a given momentum change).
- Air bags can be dangerous if a passenger isn't properly restrained / isn't wearing a seat belt.
- This is because passengers who aren't properly restrained keep moving forwards in a crash and hit the air bag whilst it is still inflating / with a lot of force.
- This risk can be reduced by wearing a seat belt at all times.
- Air bags are also dangerous if used with rear-facing child seats.
- This is because the air bag inflates behind the child seat, so can throw the child into the car seat with a lot of force.
- This risk can be reduced by not placing rear-facing child seats in seats where an air bag is fitted.

Module 4: Section 1 — Electricity

Page 59 — Charge, Current and Potential Difference

1 Time in seconds = $10 \times 60 = 600$ s
$I = \Delta Q / \Delta t = 4500 / 600 =$ **7.5 A** *[1 mark]*

2 Energy transferred to water = 0.88 × electrical energy input
so the energy input will be 308 / 0.88 = 350 J *[1 mark]*
$W = VQ$ so $Q = W / V$
$Q = 350 / 230 =$ **1.5 C (to 2 s.f.)** *[1 mark]*
The heat energy that the kettle transfers to the water is less than the electrical energy input because the kettle is less than 100% efficient.

3 $I = Anev$ so $v = I / Ane$
so $v = 13 \div ((5.0 \times 10^{-6}) \times (1.0 \times 10^{29}) \times (1.60 \times 10^{-19}))$ *[1 mark]*
= **1.6 × 10⁻⁴ ms⁻¹ (to 2 s.f.)** *[1 mark]*

Page 61 — Resistance and Resistivity

1 Area = $\pi r^2 = \pi(d/2)^2$ and $d = 1.0 \times 10^{-3}$ m
so area = $\pi \times (0.5 \times 10^{-3})^2 = 7.853... \times 10^{-7}$ m² *[1 mark]*
$R = \rho L / A = (2.8 \times 10^{-8} \times 4) \div 7.853... \times 10^{-7}$ *[1 mark]*
= **0.14 Ω (to 2 s.f.)** *[1 mark]*

2 a) $R = V / I = 7.00 \div (9.33 \times 10^{-3}) = 750.267...$
= **750 Ω (to 3 s.f.)** *[1 mark]*

b) For $V = 3.00$ V, $R = 3.00 \div (4.00 \times 10^{-3}) = 750$ Ω
for $V = 11.00$ V, $R = 11.00 \div (14.67 \times 10^{-3}) = 749.82...$ Ω *[1 mark]*
The component is an ohmic conductor (for the range considered) *[1 mark]*, because there is no significant change in resistance for different potential differences *[1 mark]*.

Page 63 — I-V Characteristics

1 a)

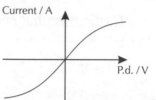

[1 mark]

b) E.g. The gradient of the I-V curve for a filament bulb gets shallower as the potential difference increases, whereas the gradient of the I-V curve for a thermistor gets steeper as the potential difference increases *[1 mark]*. For both a filament bulb and a thermistor, increasing the voltage and therefore the current increases the temperature of the circuit component *[1 mark]*. For a filament bulb, increasing the temperature increases the resistance, as it causes the metal ions in the wire filament to vibrate more, causing the charge carrying electrons to collide with them more frequently and impeding their flow *[1 mark]*. For a thermistor, increasing the temperature decreases the resistance as it releases more charge carriers *[1 mark]*.

Page 65 — Electrical Energy and Power

1 a) $I = P / V = 920 / 230 =$ **4.00 A (to 3 s.f.)** *[1 mark]*

b) $I = V / R = 230 / 190 = 1.210... =$ **1.21 A (to 3 s.f.)** *[1 mark]*

c) $P_{motor} = VI = 230 \times 1.210... = 278.421...$ W *[1 mark]*
Total power = motor power + heater power
= 278.421... + 920 = **1.20 kW (to 3 s.f.)** *[1 mark]*
You could also answer this question by calculating using
$P_{total} = V_{total}I_{total}$ *where* $V_{total} = 230$ V *(the source p.d.) and*
$I_{total} = 4.00 + 1.210...$ A.

2 a) Energy transferred = $W = VIt = 12 \times 48 \times 2.0$
= **1150 J (to 3 s.f)** *[1 mark]*

b) Energy wasted in wires = $W = I^2Rt = 48^2 \times 0.01 \times 2.0$
= **46 J (to 2 s.f)** *[1 mark]*

Answers

Page 67 — Domestic Energy and Energy Saving

1 a) $W = Pt$
   i) $W = 1550 \times (15 \times 60) = $ **1 400 000 J (to 3 s.f.)** *[1 mark]*
   ii) $W = 1.55 \times (15 \div 60)$
       $= 0.3875 = $ **0.388 kWh (to 3 s.f.)** *[1 mark]*
  b) Cost = number of units × price per unit
        $= 0.3875 \times 15.9 = $ **6.16p (to 3 s.f.)** *[1 mark]*

2   $P = VI = 230 \times (6.5 \times 10^{-3}) = 1.495 \text{ W} = 0.001495 \text{ kW}$ *[1 mark]*
   $W = Pt = 0.001495 \times 10 = 0.01495$ kWh *[1 mark]*
   Cost $= 0.01495 \times 16.2 = 0.24219 = $ **0.24p (to 2 s.f.)** *[1 mark]*

3 a) $W = Pt$
    Model A: $W = 0.47 \times (135 \div 60)$
              $= 1.0575 = $ **1.06 kWh (to 3 s.f.)** *[1 mark]*
    Model B: $W = 0.41 \times (125 \div 60)$
               $= 0.85416... = $ **0.854 kWh (to 3 s.f.)** *[1 mark]*
  b) Weeks in a year = 52, so the customer will do 52 × 2 = 104 loads.
    Model A:
    Energy used per year = 1.0575 × 104 = 109.98 kWh *[1 mark]*
    Cost per year = 109.98 × 16.2 = **1780p (to 3 s.f.)** (or £17.80)
    [1 mark]
    Model B:
    Energy used per year = 0.854... × 104 = 88.833... kWh *[1 mark]*
    Cost per year = 88.833... × 16.2 = **1440p (to 3 s.f.)** (or £14.40)
    [1 mark]

Page 69 — E.m.f and Internal Resistance

1 a) $\varepsilon = I(R + r)$ so $I = \varepsilon / (R + r)$
                $= 24 / (4.0 + 0.8) = $ **5.0 A** *[1 mark]*
  b) $V = IR = 5.0 \times 4.0 = $ **20 V** *[1 mark]*
    You could also have used $\varepsilon = V + Ir$.

2   C *[1 mark]*
   $\varepsilon = I(R + r)$, but since there are two cells in series replace r with $2r$, and ε with 2ε, then rearrange to find I

Page 71 — Conservation of Charge & Energy in Circuits

1 a) Resistance of parallel resistors:
    $1/R_{parallel} = 1/6.0 + 1/3.0 = 1/2$
    $R_{parallel} = 2.0 \, \Omega$ *[1 mark]*
    Total resistance:
    $R_{total} = 4.0 + R_{parallel} = 4.0 + 2.0 = $ **6.0 Ω** *[1 mark]*
  b) $V = I_3 R_{total}$ so rearranging $I_3 = V / R_{total} = 12 / 6.0$
                           = 2.0 A *[1 mark]*
  c) $V = IR = 2.0 \times 4.0 = $ **8.0 V** *[1 mark]*
  d) E.m.f. = sum of p.d.s in circuit, so $12 = 8.0 + V_{parallel}$
    $V_{parallel} = 12 - 8.0 = $ **4.0 V** *[1 mark]*
  e) $I = V/R$, so
    $I_1 = 4.0 / 3.0 = $ **1.3 A (to 2 s.f.)** *[1 mark]*
    $I_2 = 4.0 / 6.0 = $ **0.67 A (to 2 s.f.)** *[1 mark]*
    You can check your answers by making sure that $I_3 = I_2 + I_1$.

Page 73 — The Potential Divider

1 a) $V_A / V_B = R_A / R_B$ so $V_A = V_B \times (R_A / R_B)$
                    $= 6.75 \times (35 \div 45) = $ **5.25 V** *[1 mark]*
  b) Input p.d. $= V_A + V_B = 5.25 + 6.75 = $ **12 V** *[1 mark]*
  c) $V_B = \dfrac{R_B}{R_A + R_B} V_{in} = \dfrac{45}{75 + 45} \times 12 = $ **4.5 V** *[1 mark]*

2 a) $V_{AB} = \dfrac{R_2}{R_1 + R_2} V_{in} = (50 / (30 + 50)) \times 12 = 7.5 \text{ V}$ *[1 mark]*
    Ignore the 10 Ω — no current flows that way.
  b) Total resistance R_T of the parallel circuit:
    $1/R_T = 1 / 50 + 1 / (10 + 40) = 1 / 25$
    $R_T = 25 \, \Omega$ *[1 mark]*
    Use $V_{out} = (R_2 / (R_1 + R_2) V_{in}$ to find the p.d. over the whole
    parallel arrangement: $(25 / (30 + 25)) \times 12 = 5.454... \text{ V}$ *[1 mark]*
    Use $V_{out} = (R_2 / R_1 + R_2) V_{in}$ again to find the p.d. across AB:
      $V_{AB} = 40 / (40 + 10) \times 5.454... = 4.363...$
         $= $ **4.4 V (to 2 s.f.)** *[1 mark]*
    current through 40 Ω resistor $= V/R$
    $= 4.363... / 40 = $ **0.11 A (to 2 s.f.)** *[1 mark]*
    This question might look tricky, but it's basically just one potential divider on top of another.

Module 4: Section 2 — Waves

Page 75 — Wave Basics

1 a) The gain is set to 2.0 volts/div and the trace
    has a maximum amplitude of 2 divisions.
    So, the maximum voltage $= 2 \times 2.0 = $ **4.0 V** *[1 mark]*
  b) One wavelength spans 3 divisions, so
    $T = 3 \times 3.0 \text{ ms} = 9.0 \text{ ms} = 9.0 \times 10^{-3} \text{ s}$ *[1 mark]*
    $f = 1/T = 1 / 9.0 \times 10^{-3}$ *[1 mark]*
    $f = 111.1... = $ **110 Hz (to 2 s.f.)** *[1 mark]*
  c) $v = f\lambda$ so $\lambda = v / f$
    $\lambda = 280/111.1...$ *[1 mark]*
    $\lambda = 2.52 \text{ m} = $ **2.5 m (to 2 s.f.)** *[1 mark]*

Page 77 — Types of Wave

1 a) $I = P \div A = 10.0 \div 0.002 = $ **5000 Wm⁻²** *[1 mark]*
  b) D *[1 mark]*

Page 79 — Polarisation of Waves

1 a) They are at right angles to one another (90°, 270° etc.) *[1 mark]*.
  b) It would be half of the intensity of the original light *[1 mark]*.
    This is because at 45° the vertical and horizontal contributions are equal, so the intensity is halved between them.
  c) Any of: Polaroid sunglasses or 3D film glasses *[1 mark]*.

Answers

Page 81 — Diffraction and Reflection

1   When a wavefront meets an obstacle, the waves will diffract round the corners of the obstacle. When the obstacle is much bigger than the wavelength, little diffraction occurs. In this case, the mountain is much bigger than the wavelength of short-wave radio. So the "shadow" where you cannot pick up short wave is very long *[1 mark]*.

[1 mark]

When the obstacle is comparable in size to the wavelength, as it is for the long-wave radio waves, more diffraction occurs. The wavefront re-forms after a shorter distance, leaving a shorter "shadow" *[1 mark]*.

2   E.g. Set up a ripple tank, using an oscillating paddle to create straight, parallel waves. Place two objects into the water, creating a barrier with a gap in the middle *[1 mark]*. Vary the sizes of the objects to increase and decrease the gap width. Observe the amount of diffraction of the water waves as the gap width varies *[1 mark]*. The most diffraction will be seen when the gap is roughly the same size as the wavelength of the water waves *[1 mark]*.

Page 83 — Refraction and Refractive Index

1 a) $n_{diamond} = c / v = (3.00 \times 10^8) / (1.24 \times 10^8) = 2.419...$
   = **2.42 (to 3 s.f.)** *[1 mark]*

b) $n_{air} \sin \theta_i = n_{diamond} \sin \theta_r$, $n_{air} = 1$
   So, $n_{diamond} = \sin \theta_i / \sin \theta_r$ *[1 mark]*
   $\sin \theta_r = \sin 50 / 2.419... = 0.316...$
   $\theta_r = \sin^{-1}(0.316...) = 18.459... = $ **18° (to 2 s.f.)** *[1 mark]*
   You can assume the refractive index of air is 1, and don't forget to write the degree sign in your answer.

2 a) When the light is pointing steeply upwards some of it is refracted and some reflected — the beam emerging from the surface is the refracted part *[1 mark]*.
   However when the beam hits the surface at more than the critical angle (to the normal to the boundary) refraction does not occur. All the beam is totally internally reflected to light the tank, hence its brightness *[1 mark]*.

b) The critical angle is $90° - 41.25° = 48.75°$ *[1 mark]*.
   $n_{water} = 1 / \sin C$
   $= 1 / \sin 48.75°$
   $= 1 / 0.7518... = 1.3300... = $ **1.330 (to 4 s.f.)** *[1 mark]*
   The question talks about the angle between the light beam and the floor of the aquarium. This angle is 90° minus the incident angle — measured from a normal to the surface of the water.

Page 85 — Superposition and Coherence

1 a) The frequencies and wavelengths of the two sources must be equal *[1 mark]* and the phase difference must be constant *[1 mark]*.

b) Interference will only be noticeable if the amplitudes of the two waves are approximately equal *[1 mark]*.

2   B *[1 mark]*

Page 87 — Two-Source Interference

1 a)
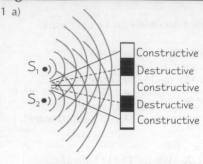

[1 mark for correct placement of constructive interference patterns, 1 mark for correct placement of destructive interference patterns]

b) Light waves from separate sources are not coherent, as light is emitted in random bursts of energy. To get coherent light the two sets of waves must emerge from one source *[1 mark]*. A laser is used because it emits coherent light that is all of one wavelength *[1 mark]*.

2 a) $\lambda = v / f = 330 / 1320 = $ **0.25 m** *[1 mark]*.

b) Separation $= x = \lambda D / a$
   $= 0.25 \text{ m} \times 7 \text{ m} / 1.5 \text{ m}$ *[1 mark]* = **1.2 m (to 2 s.f.)** *[1 mark]*.

Page 89 — Diffraction Gratings

1 a) Use $\sin \theta = n\lambda / d$
   For the first order, $n = 1$
   So, $\sin \theta = \lambda / d$ *[1 mark]*
   No need to actually work out d. The number of lines per metre is 1 / d. So you can simply multiply the wavelength by that.
   $\sin \theta = 6.00 \times 10^{-7} \times 4.0 \times 10^5 = 0.24$
   $\theta = \sin^{-1}(0.24) = 13.8865... = $ **14° (to 2 s.f.)** *[1 mark]*
   For the second order, $n = 2$ and $\sin \theta = 2\lambda / d$. *[1 mark]*
   You already have a value for λ / d. Just double it to get sin θ for the second order.
   $\sin \theta = 0.48$
   $\theta = \sin^{-1}(0.48) = 28.685... = $ **29° (to 2 s.f.)** *[1 mark]*

b) No. Putting $n = 5$ into the equation gives a value of $\sin \theta$ of 1.2, which is impossible *[1 mark]*.

2   $\sin \theta = n\lambda / d$, so for the 1st order maximum, $\sin \theta = \lambda / d$
   $\sin 14.2° = \lambda \times 3.70 \times 10^5$ *[1 mark]*
   $\lambda = $ **663 nm (or 6.63×10^{-7} m) (to 3 s.f.)** *[1 mark]*.

Page 91 — Stationary (Standing) Waves

1 a)
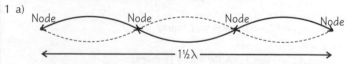

[1 mark for the correct shape, 1 mark for labelling the length]

b) For a string vibrating at three times the first harmonic,
   length $= 3\lambda / 2$
   $1.2 \text{ m} = 3\lambda / 2$
   $\lambda = $ **0.8 m** *[1 mark]*

c) When the string forms a standing wave, its amplitude varies from a maximum at the antinodes to zero at the nodes *[1 mark]*. In a progressive wave all the points have the same amplitude *[1 mark]*

2   Distance between nodes $= \lambda/2$ *[1 mark]*
   $\lambda = 2 \times 15.0 \text{ cm} = 30.0 \text{ cm} = 0.30 \text{ m}$ *[1 mark]*
   $v = f\lambda$ so $v = 1.00 \times 10^9 \times 0.30$ *[1 mark]*
   $v = $ **3.0×10^8 ms^{-1}** *[1 mark]*

Answers

Module 4: Section 3 — Quantum Physics

Page 93— Light — Wave or Particle

1 a) At threshold voltage:

$E_{kinetic}$ of an electron = E_{photon} emitted *[1 mark]*

So $E_{photon} = e \times V = 1.60 \times 10^{-19} \times 1.70 = \mathbf{2.72 \times 10^{-19}}$ **J** *[1 mark]*

b) $E = \dfrac{hc}{\lambda}$ so $h = \dfrac{E\lambda}{c}$

$\lambda = 7.00 \times 10^{-7}$, $c = 3.00 \times 10^{8}$

So, $h = \dfrac{2.72 \times 10^{-19} \times 7.00 \times 10^{-7}}{3.00 \times 10^{8}}$ *[1 mark]*

$= 6.346.... \times 10^{-34}$

$= \mathbf{6.35 \times 10^{-34}}$ **Js (to 3 s.f.)** *[1 mark]*

Page 95 — The Photoelectric Effect

1 $\phi = 2.9$ eV $= 2.9 \times (1.60 \times 10^{-19})$ J $= 4.64 \times 10^{-19}$ J *[1 mark]*

$f = \dfrac{\phi}{h} = \dfrac{4.64 \times 10^{-19}}{6.63 \times 10^{-34}} = 6.99... \times 10^{14}$

$= \mathbf{7.0 \times 10^{14}}$ **Hz (to 2 s.f.)** *[1 mark]*

2 a) $E = hf$

$= (6.63 \times 10^{-34}) \times (2.0 \times 10^{15}) = 1.326 \times 10^{-18}$ J *[1 mark]*

1.326×10^{-18} J $= \dfrac{1.326 \times 10^{-18}}{1.60 \times 10^{-19}}$ eV

$= 8.2875 = \mathbf{8.3}$ **eV (to 2 s.f.)** *[1 mark]*

b) $E_{photon} = E_{max\,kinetic} + \phi$

$E_{max\,kinetic} = E_{photon} - \phi$

$= 8.2875 - 4.7 = 3.5875$ *[1 mark]*

$= \mathbf{3.6}$ **eV (to 2 s.f.) (or** 5.7×10^{-19} **J)** *[1 mark]*

3 An electron needs to gain a certain amount of energy (the work function energy) before it can leave the surface of the metal *[1 mark]*.
If the energy carried by each photon is less than this work function energy, no electrons will be emitted *[1 mark]*.

Page 97 — Wave-Particle Duality

1 a) Electromagnetic radiation can show characteristics of both particles and waves *[1 mark]*.

b) $\lambda = \dfrac{h}{p}$

so $p = \dfrac{h}{\lambda}$ *[1 mark]*

$= \dfrac{6.63 \times 10^{-34}}{590 \times 10^{-9}} = 1.123... \times 10^{-27}$

$= \mathbf{1.1 \times 10^{-27}}$ **kg ms^{-1} (to 2 s.f.)** *[1 mark]*

2 a) $\lambda = \dfrac{h}{p} = \dfrac{h}{mv}$

$\lambda = \dfrac{6.63 \times 10^{-34}}{9.11 \times 10^{-31} \times 3.50 \times 10^{6}}$ *[1 mark]*

$= 2.079... \times 10^{-10}$

$= \mathbf{2.08 \times 10^{-10}}$ **m (to 3 s.f.)** *[1 mark]*

b) Either $\lambda = \dfrac{h}{p} = \dfrac{h}{mv}$

So $v = \dfrac{h}{m\lambda} = \dfrac{6.63 \times 10^{-34}}{1.673 \times 10^{-27} \times 2.079... \times 10^{-10}}$ *[1 mark]*

$= 1905.85... = \mathbf{1910}$ **ms^{-1} (to 3 s.f.)** *[1 mark]*

Or momentum of protons = momentum of electrons

so $m_p \times v_p = m_e \times v_e$

$v_p = v_e \times \dfrac{m_e}{m_p} = 3.50 \times 10^{6} \times \dfrac{9.11 \times 10^{-31}}{1.673 \times 10^{-27}}$ *[1 mark]*

$= 1905.85... = \mathbf{1910}$ **ms^{-1} (to 3 s.f.)** *[1 mark]*

c) The proton has a larger mass, so it will have a smaller speed, since the two have the same kinetic energy *[1 mark]*. Kinetic energy is proportional to the square of the speed, while momentum is proportional to the speed, so they will have different momenta *[1 mark]*. Wavelength depends on the momentum, so the wavelengths are different *[1 mark]*.

This is a really hard question. If you didn't get it right, make sure you understand the answer fully. Do the algebra if it helps.

3 B *[1 mark]*

Index

Index

Index

PRAR53